Prentice Hall
LITERATURE
Timeless Voices, Timeless Themes

Reading Diagnostic Tests and Improvement Plan

Prentice Hall

Upper Saddle River, New Jersey
Glenview, Illinois
Needham, Massachusetts

Acknowledgments

Arena Press

Excerpts from *Reading Sourcebook* by Bill Hornig, Linda Diamond, and Linda Gutlohn. Copyright 2000 by CORE. "Core Phenome Segmentation Test" by Orna Lencher, PhD, from *Assessing Reading: Multiple Measures.* Copyright 1999 by CORE. All rights reserved. Reprinted with permission of Arena Press, Novato, CA.

International Reading Association

"San Diego Quick Assessment" by Margaret Lea Pray et al, from *The Graded Word List: Quick Gauge of Reading Ability.* Copyright © by M.H. La Pray and the International Reading Association. All rights reserved.

ISBN 0-13-062841-7

2 3 4 5 6 7 8 9 10   05 04 03 02

Contents

Introduction: Using the Reading Diagnostic Test and Improvement Plan

Before beginning to use the *Prentice Hall Reading Achievement System*, be sure to administer the Student Placement Screening Test to determine if any of your students are lacking prerequisite skills necessary for them to succeed. Use screening in conjunction with students' standardized test scores and academic records to plan appropriate curriculum with intervention strategies. The *Prentice Hall Language Arts Skills Intervention System* provides instruction for such students.

The assessments in this book will help you identify students' strengths and weaknesses in order to monitor their reading development and determine causes of reading difficulties. They will help you plan for appropriate instruction and direct you to ways to help students overcome their weaknesses and improve their reading skills. The assessments consist of Diagnostic Tests and Mastery Tests as well as additional tests for reading fluency.

The Diagnostic Tests will help you assess students' proficiency in a wide variety of reading skills. Students who do not show proficiency in certain skills can then be taught these skills in lessons in the *Basic Reading Skills: Comprehensive Lessons for Improvement*. At the end of the year, or at any chosen point during the year, the Mastery Tests can be given to assess students' mastery of the skills.

Since students in grades 6 to 8 may have a wide range of reading abilities, assessment begins broadly. For students who pass the Student Placement Screening Test, you administer tests to determine how well students can comprehend text, analyze literature, and understand vocabulary. If students do well on these tests, then no other diagnostic tests need to be given. However, you can use the tests results to determine what specific skills may need additional instruction. If students show deficiencies in reading comprehension and vocabulary skills, then administer tests to assess reading fluency and word recognition. Low ratings on these tests indicate that the student has a problem with decoding text (the ability to convert the printed word into a representation of the oral language). To diagnose which decoding skills are deficient, administer tests in phonic elements and phonemic awareness. The Assessment and Improvement Plan flow chart on the next page shows the sequence for testing and plan for instruction for improvement.

Administering Tests

The Diagnostic Tests should be administered at the beginning of the year. Because of the number of skills assessed, the tests will need to be administered over several days. The first set of tests to be given are multiple-choice. Because the tests on Reading Comprehension and on Literary Response and Analysis include reading passages, they will take more time to complete. Therefore, these tests are organized into modules by topics, and

Assessment and Improvement Plan

Diagnostic Test	Test Results	Further Assessment	Plan for Improvement
Reading Comprehension Literary Response and Analysis Vocabulary and Concept Development	2–3 items correct on majority of sets of questions in each test*	No further assessment indicated	Regular instruction, including lessons for some skills as needed**
	0–1 items correct on majority of sets of questions in each test*	Take next level of assessment	Teach lessons on deficient skills**
Oral Reading Fluency San Diego Quick Assessment of Reading Ability	Ratings of fluent and independent	No further assessment indicated	Regular instruction
	Ratings other than fluent and independent	Take next level of assessment	Teach Decoding and Word Recognition Lessons 1–3**
Phonic Elements	60% of items correct	No further assessment indicated	No intervention needed
	Less than 60% of items correct	Take next level of assessment	Further evaluation to determine specific intervention needed
CORE Phoneme Segmentation	Does not complete test accurately	Repeat test after intervention	Needs intensive intervention

*Consider the number of correct items for lower-level skills compared with higher-level skills to determine if more assessment is needed.

**Lessons in *Basic Reading Skills: Comprehensive Lessons for Improvement.* See charts on pages I-5 to I-12.

they vary in length. Preview these tests and decide if you want to administer more than one module at a time. Mastery Tests can be administered at the end of the year, or specific modules can be administered after students complete the appropriate lessons. For students who have problems with reading fluency, two additional Oral Reading Fluency Tests are provided to assess progress during the year.

Directions and sample questions are provided at the beginning of each multiple-choice test module. It is recommended that you go over the directions and sample questions with the class before administering the test. Directions call for students to fill in the bubble on the answer sheet. Student Answer Sheets in the back of this book will need to be reproduced for students.

All of the other tests except for Phonic Elements need to be administered orally to individual students: Oral Reading Fluency Test, San Diego Quick Assessment of Reading Ability, and CORE Phoneme Segmentation Test. Each of these tests come with specific directions for administration and a Student Record Form for recording results as the test is given. Once you have determined which students need to take any of these tests, you will need to schedule administration. First, you will need to preview the directions to determine what supplies you will need and how long the test will take.

Prescribing Lessons Based on Test Results

Use the Assessment and Improvement Plan chart as a general guide for determining when to teach lessons to improve reading skills of students who show deficiencies based on results of the Diagnostic Tests. You can group students with similar deficiencies for teaching certain lessons. The charts on the next few pages indicate which skills are assessed by which test item in Diagnostic and Mastery Tests, and which lessons teach that skill. Students who get two of three multiple-choice test items incorrect for a skill should receive instruction using the corresponding lesson in *Basic Reading Skills: Comprehensive Lessons for Improvement*. A few items assess skills more than two grades below grade level. If a student scores poorly on these items, consider complete test results, along with student records, to determine the student's special needs and to plan appropriate curriculum with intervention strategies.

For oral tests, students are given ratings according to criteria described in the directions for administering the test. Information for interpreting results of each test is provided below.

- **Oral Reading Fluency Tests:** Students are rated at three levels: fluent, somewhat fluent, or limited fluency. Lessons on fluency should be taught to any student not rated as fluent. Students with limited fluency will need additional practice with fluency using the strategies provided in the lessons.

- **San Diego Quick Assessment of Reading Ability:** Students are rated at three levels: independent, instructional, or frustration. The student's reading level is the last grade-level word list read with eight or more correct words. Students reading at the frustration level at or below grade level need further assessment to determine the cause of poor word recognition.
- **CORE Phoneme Segmentation Test:** Students who cannot complete the entire test are lacking phoneme awareness skills. They need intervention in phoneme awareness and decoding skills.

Diagnosing and Prescribing Instruction

Reading Comprehension

Skills in Test Modules and Lessons	Diagnostic Test Items	Basic Reading Skills Lesson	Mastery Test Items
Using and Analyzing Structural Features			
Using text features to make text usable	1–3	1	1–3
Using structural features of popular media to obtain information	4–6	2	4–6
Using a variety of documents to locate information	7–9	3	7–9
Understanding structure and purpose of informational materials	10–12	4	10–12
Identifying structural patterns in informational text	13–15	No lesson*	13–15
Analyzing text using sequential or chronological organization	16–18	7	16–18
Analyzing text using compare-and-contrast organization	19–21	8	19–21
Analyzing text using cause-and-effect organization	22–24	9	22–24
Evaluating Text			
Using strategies for different reading purposes	1–3	No lesson*	1–3
Identifying main idea and supporting details in expository text	4–6	12	4–6
Connecting main ideas	7–9	13	7–9
Making and confirming predictions using text clues	10–12	No lesson*	10–12
Distinguishing cause and effect	13–15	15	13–15
Distinguishing between fact and opinion	16–18	16	16–18

*Diagnostic Test and Mastery Test items assess prerequisite skills for subsequent lessons.

Skills in Test Modules and Lessons	Diagnostic Test Items	Basic Reading Skills Lesson	Mastery Test Items
Evaluating Text			
Distinguishing facts, opinions, and supported inferences	19–21	17	19–21
Making inferences from prior knowledge and text clues	22–24	18	22–24
Comparing information from several sources	25–27	No lesson*	25–27
Making assertions about a text	28–30	20	28–30
Evaluating new information and hypotheses	31–33	No lesson*	31–33
Noting unsupported inferences, fallacious reasoning, and propaganda	34–36	22	34–36
Evaluating author's conclusions	37–39	23	37–39
Tracing the development of the author's argument	40–42	24	40–42
Assessing the author's evidence	43–45	25	43–45
Locating and Using Information			
Following instructions in a technical manual	1–3	No lesson*	1–3
Following multiple-step instructions for preparing applications	4–6	29	4–6
Understanding how to use simple mechanical devices by following directions	7–9	30	7–9
Creating outlines and notes	10–12	31	10–12

*Diagnostic Test and Mastery Test items assess prerequisite skills for subsequent lessons.

Literary Response and Analysis

Skills in Test Modules and Lessons	Diagnostic Test Items	Basic Reading Skills Lesson	Mastery Test Items
Structural Features			
Describing structural differences in imaginative forms of literature	1–4	No lesson*	1–4
Identifying and analyzing characteristics of forms of literature	5–8	2	5–8
Describing the major characteristics of forms of fiction	9–12	3	9–13
Articulating purposes and characteristics of forms of prose	13–15	4	14–16
Narrative Analysis: Story Elements			
Identifying the main events in a plot	1–3	No lesson*	1–3
Identifying the plot conflict and explaining its resolution	4–6	7	4–6
Determining how events advance the plot	7–9	8	7–9
Determining causes of a character's actions	10–12	No lesson*	10–12
Comparing one character type across cultures	13–15	No lesson*	13–15
Contrasting characters' appearance, actions, and motives	16–18	12	16–18
Analyzing the effect of qualities of characters on plot	19–21	13	19–21
Analyzing characterization	22–24	14	22–24
Analyzing the influence of setting on a problem and its resolution	25–27	16	25–27
Narrative Analysis: Author's Technique and Language			
Recognizing themes in works	1–3	18	1–3
Identifying and analyzing features of themes	4–6	19	4–6

*Diagnostic Test and Mastery Test items assess prerequisite skills for subsequent lessons.

Skills in Test Modules and Lessons	Diagnostic Test Items	Basic Reading Skills Lesson	Mastery Test Items
Narrative Analysis: Author's Technique and Language			
Identifying and analyzing recurring themes across works	7–9	20	7–9
Defining figurative language and identifying its literary use	10–14	No lesson*	10–14
Describing the function and effect of common literary devices	15–17	23	15–17
Explaining the effects of common literary devices in fiction and nonfiction	18–21	24	18–21
Recognizing differences in first- and third-person narration	22–24	26	22–24
Explaining how points of view contribute to overall effects of works	25–27	27	25–27
Defining how tone or meaning is conveyed in poetry	28–30	28	28–30
Literary Criticism			
Evaluating the meaning of archetypal patterns and symbols across cultures	1–3	29	1–3
Evaluating the author's use of various techniques	4–6	30	4–6
Critiquing contrived and realistic plot situations and credibility of characterization	7–9	31	7–9
Analyzing responses to literary works	10–12	32	10–12

*Diagnostic Test and Mastery Test items assess prerequisite skills for subsequent lessons.

Vocabulary and Concept Development

Skills in Test Modules and Lessons	Diagnostic Test Items	Basic Reading Skills Lesson	Mastery Test Items
Using antonyms	1–3	No lesson*	1–3
Using synonyms	4–6	No lesson*	4–6
Explaining frequently used synonyms, antonyms, and homographs	1–9	4	1–9
Using root words	10–12	No lesson*	10–12
Using common and abstract Greek and Latin roots and affixes	13–18	6	13–18
Using word structure to understand content-area vocabulary	19–21	7	19–21
Applying knowledge of word origins	22–24	8	22–24
Using word origins	25–27	9	25–27
Recognizing origins and meanings of foreign words used in English	28–30	10	28–30
Using context clues to understand words with novel meanings	31–33	12	31–33
Using definitions and restatements to clarify word meanings	34–37	13	34–37
Interpreting words with multiple meanings	37–39	No lesson*	37–39
Understanding shades of meaning in related words	40–42	16	40–42
Understanding figurative and metaphorical use of words	58–60	17	58–60

*Diagnostic Test and Mastery Test items assess prerequisite skills for subsequent lessons.

Skills in Test Modules and Lessons	Diagnostic Test Items	Basic Reading Skills Lesson	Mastery Test Items
Interpreting figurative language and words with multiple meanings	61–63	18	61–63
Using idioms	43–45	No lesson*	43–45
Identifying idioms	46–48	19	46–48
Identifying analogies	49–51	21	49–51
Identifying metaphors	52–54	23	52–54
1Identifying similes	55–57	25	55–57
Using a thesaurus	64–66	No lesson*	64–66

*Diagnostic Test and Mastery Test items assess prerequisite skills for subsequent lessons.

Decoding and Word Recognition

Skills in Test Modules and Lessons	Diagnostic Test Items	Basic Reading Skills Lesson	Mastery Test Items
Oral Reading Fluency			
Reading text aloud fluently and accurately and with appropriate pacing, intonation, and expression	Oral Reading Fluency Test	1–3	Oral Reading Fluency Test

Diagnostic Test
Reading Comprehension
Using and Analyzing Structural Features

Directions for all questions in this test:

Read each passage and answer the questions that follow it. Some items will have no passage. On the answer sheet, fill in the bubble for the answer you think is correct.

Sample questions:

> Grandmother's house was very different from Carrie's. Grandmother lived in a small house near a lake. Other houses were around the lake, but there was a lot of space between them, and not many people lived there. Carrie lived in a large apartment building in the city. Hundreds of other families lived in the same building. Her neighborhood was filled with all sorts of buildings right next to one another. It was an exciting place, but sometimes Carrie wished it was as quiet as Grandmother's neighborhood.

1. Which of these is compared in this story?
   A. the kind of people in each neighborhood
   B. the number of people in each neighborhood
   C. the cost of living in each neighborhood
   D. the things you can do in each neighborhood

2. Which of these tells you what is in each chapter of a book?
   A. the copyright
   B. the glossary
   C. the table of contents
   D. the index

1. How does a *caption* help you understand the contents of a book or magazine article?
   A. It tells you what page information is on.
   B. It organizes information about related topics.
   C. It defines the meanings of words.
   D. It explains what a picture is about.

2. Books, newspaper stories, and magazine articles often contain major heads and subheads. These headings are sometimes printed in bold type. What is the purpose of a head or a subhead?
   A. It explains who wrote the story and took the pictures.
   B. It summarizes the information in that section of the story.
   C. It lets you know why the author wrote the story.
   D. It explains where you can learn more information.

3. Books, magazines, and newspapers often use graphs to help readers understand stories. What is the purpose of a graph?
   A. A graph is like an outline.
   B. A graph defines hard words that are found in a book.
   C. A graph summarizes information in a visual way.
   D. A graph makes the reader stop and think.

4. Jason did an Internet news search and found an article about hurricanes. On the screen is a button that says ILLUS. If he clicks on this button, he will probably see
   A. pictures of a hurricane.
   B. the origin of the word "hurricane."
   C. the dates of famous hurricanes.
   D. a description of how hurricanes are formed.

5. Which of these would probably be on the front page of a newspaper with a big headline?
   A. the times that a new store in town will be open
   B. where the traffic will be heaviest that day
   C. what kind of food you can make for an outdoor party
   D. a story about the winner of the election for president

6. Newspapers, magazines, and television news shows sometimes do a *series* about an important topic. This means they do part of the story each day for several days. Why do you think they do this?
   A. It helps people who can't read very fast.
   B. The story is good, and they want it to last a long time.
   C. There is too much information to put in just one story.
   D. The writers aren't sure if people will like the story.

Are you tired of your dog taking you for walks? Try the Soft Touch collar and leash system. With Soft Touch, you can train your dog to follow your lead naturally. When your dog tries to run out in front of you and drag you along, just hold the leash gently but firmly, and the dog will naturally turn to face you. In this position, it is impossible for the dog to drag you down the sidewalk.

7. The Soft Touch system would be most useful for people who
   A. have more dogs than they can handle.
   B. like to go running with their dogs.
   C. want to teach their dogs some tricks.
   D. have dogs that are difficult to control.

Telephones, faxes, and computers are company property and should be used for company business only. This includes voice mail, electronic mail, and computer files. Employees may need to use these communication tools for personal reasons from time to time. If and when that time comes, employees should keep their personal use to a minimum and should do so only during nonwork hours such as lunchtime.

8. When may employees at this company use the telephone for personal reasons?
   A. when work is slow
   B. when taking an official break
   C. whenever they need to
   D. whenever their boss approves

Metro's garbage haulers will pick up household yard refuse every other Friday beginning January 4th. On pick-up day, each household in the Metro area can set out one 32-gallon trash can, one paper yard bag, or one bundle of trimmings at no charge. Any additional cans, bags, or bundles will cost the household $1.50 each. Please note that the bags, cans, and bundles cannot exceed 45 pounds each.

9. Which statement is true about Metro's service?
   A. Each can, bag, and bundle cannot weigh more than 32 pounds.
   B. Household garbage is picked up at the same time yard refuse is.
   C. Every two weeks, one can, bag, or bundle is picked up for free.
   D. The fee for a household's first 45 cans, bags, or bundles is $1.50.

All clothes are not created equal. That's why Windmark has made its latest washing machine, the T1100 Deluxe. With five speed settings, the T1100 can handle your messiest mud stains and your most delicate hand-washable fabrics. The T1100 also offers a second rinse option for those tough stains.

10. This paragraph would most likely be found in
   A. an advertisement.
   B. an owner's manual.
   C. a sales agreement.
   D. a set of directions.

Your Windmark T1100 Deluxe is covered under warranty for ten years after the purchase date of the machine. This warranty does not cover damages caused by natural disasters or damage to the washing machine due to the owner's mishandling. (See owner's manual for handling instructions.) The T1100 Deluxe will be serviced free of charge if any mechanical problems arise. The machine will be replaced if any problems continue after a service representative has attempted a repair.

11. This paragraph describes
   A. where to find information about handling the washing machine.
   B. how to fix a washing machine that someone has just bought.
   C. why the washing machine might break down after a few years.
   D. when the company will fix problems with the washing machine.

To Start Your Washer:
1. Measure detergent and add to basin.
2. Add fabric softener to dispenser in the center of machine.
3. Close washer lid and set water level.
4. Set water temperature control and number of rinses.
5. Set speed control.
6. Close lid and pull wash cycle knob out to begin washing.

12. What information do you find in this passage?
   A. list of temperature settings for a washer
   B. speeds and controls for a washer
   C. directions for starting a washer
   D. instructions for care and service of washer

Parents often tell stories about the past to their children. The stories may change over time and become more and more unbelievable. Ancient stories, called myths, are like family stories in many ways. Myths are stories about heroic warriors and the magical world of gods long ago. Like family stories, myths were passed down through history by storytellers. Though the stories may have happened, myths have many unbelievable characters and adventures.

13. This paragraph is mostly about
   A. why parents tell stories to children.
   B. ancient stories.
   C. how family stories and myths are alike.
   D. unbelievable characters.

At ten o'clock Saturday morning, the Collin County Balloon Festival was called off. Just before the balloon race was to start, large rain clouds formed. The balloon pilots thought the event should go on because they raced in freezing, windy weather last year. The judges, however, heard thunder and saw lightning a few miles off. They felt that the weather was unsafe for the balloon owners. The festival will take place later in the month.

14. Which of these is an example of a *cause* in the paragraph?
   A. unsafe weather
   B. calling off the race
   C. balloon pilots
   D. balloon owners

Young children enjoy hearing stories read aloud. Hearing stories read aloud can be enjoyable and helpful even for older students. Mrs. Dixon reads aloud to her ninth graders before each English class. She believes that students don't feel as much pressure to remember all the details of a novel when she reads it. She also has students read aloud to each other. She finds that students pay attention better when they may be called on to read. Mrs. Dixon tests students on the novels she reads to them. "Students get better scores on novels I read to them," Mrs. Dixon comments.

15. This paragraph is an example of
   A. compare/contrast.
   B. cause/effect.
   C. proposition/support.
   D. chronological order.

In the 1700s, a Russian leader named Peter the Great asked a Danish sea captain, Vitus Bering, to explore the north Pacific for Russia. During this trip, Bering is said to have reached Alaska. For many years, Alaska was controlled by Russia.

The British, Spanish, and French were also exploring the coast of Alaska. Hunters from these countries killed too many animals for their furs. They also mistreated the Native Americans who lived in Alaska at the time. In 1799, an organization called the Russian American Company was formed. It helped to control hunting.

Unfortunately, the Russians didn't improve relations with Alaska's Native Americans. Russia was involved in wars in their homelands, and the country was seriously weakened. By the 1800s, Russian leaders did not want Alaska any more. They asked the United States to buy the land.

At first, most people thought Alaska was nothing more than a wasteland. Almost no one wanted to spend any money to buy it. Finally the United States agreed to purchase Alaska. In 1867, the United States bought Alaska for about seven million dollars.

The United States government ignored Alaska for many years after that. No one knew what to do with the vast territory. Then, in the late 1800s, gold was discovered in Alaska. The huge Alaskan Gold Rush began. Thousands of people traveled to Alaska to strike it rich. Few did, but many people stayed in the area.

In 1949, people in Alaska began to work toward statehood. For nine years, Alaskans campaigned to become a state. Finally, on January 3, 1959, Alaska became the forty-ninth state in the United States.

16. Which was the first European country to control Alaska?
A. Spain
B. Russia
C. Britain
D. France

17. When it first bought Alaska, the United States government
A. discovered gold there.
B. asked Vitus Bering to explore it.
C. ignored the territory.
D. was involved in wars at home.

18. How is most of the information in this paragraph organized?
A. by time, according to when things happened in history
B. by importance, with the most important things first
C. by comparison, showing how things are alike
D. by contrast, showing how things are different

What could chocolate and Coca-Cola possibly have in common? Both contain caffeine and are popular around the world. The main ingredient in chocolate comes from the beans of the cacao tree, and the flavoring for Coke originally came from the nuts of the kola tree. Although they grow in different parts of the world, the cacao tree and the kola tree are part of the same plant family.

19. One ingredient chocolate and Coca-Cola have in common is
   A. kola nuts.
   B. caffeine.
   C. cacao beans.
   D. cocoa.

When Damien moved to a new house, he explored his new neighborhood. He noticed the big, old oak trees lining the sidewalks. His old neighborhood had smaller trees. He found some parks and playgrounds to play in. His favorite discovery was that many of the kids who lived on his new street were his age. His old neighborhood had been full of kids, too, and he missed his old friends.

20. How is Damien's new neighborhood like his old one?
   A. It has old friends.
   B. It has playgrounds.
   C. It has big, old trees.
   D. It has kids his age.

Both fluorescent and regular light bulbs are safe and give off bright light. Many people like regular bulbs because they find that the light is easier on their eyes. Regular bulbs are also cheaper than fluorescent ones. On the other hand, fluorescent bulbs use less electricity and last much longer than regular bulbs.

21. How are fluorescent bulbs different from regular ones?
   A. Fluorescent bulbs give off better light.
   B. Fluorescent bulbs use less electricity.
   C. Fluorescent bulbs are not as safe to use.
   D. Fluorescent bulbs burn out more quickly.

"Who's that?" asked Jamey.

Kayrn looked at the tall, athletic woman with gray hair tied back in a short ponytail. "Oh, that's my grandmother. She's training for the City Run next week."

The two girls finished their run and sat on the sidelines. The older woman joined them shortly.

"How's it going, Nanna?" Kayrn asked.

"Pretty good," her grandmother replied. "I cut three seconds off my best time."

Jamey looked at the older woman. "How long have you been running?" she asked.

"Most of my life," Nanna replied, "but not on a team. You girls are lucky."

"What do you mean?" Jamey asked, confused. "Women have been competing in the Olympics for years."

"True," replied Nanna. "But it's only been in the last thirty years or so that ordinary women were given the chance to run in school, in marathons, and other events. A lot of people struggled so you can play almost any sport you want."

Nanna told the girls about the old days when women had few opportunities to race. She explained how things changed when Kathryn Switzer entered the Boston Marathon in 1967. "She registered as K. Switzer so no one would know she was a woman," Nanna said. "She finished in four hours and 20 minutes, better than some men."

After she finished her story, Nanna rose to her feet and said good-bye to the girls. The girls watched Nanna as she jogged to the parking lot. "Your grandma is pretty cool," Jamey said.

Kayrn thought for a moment. "I think it's something way beyond cool," replied proudly.

22. What caused Kayrn to look over at the woman who was running?
A. The woman was running fast.
B. Jamey asked who she was.
C. Kayrn was looking for another friend.
D. The woman talked about Kathryn Switzer.

23. Why did Kathryn Switzer use her first initial when she entered the Boston Marathon?
A. Women weren't allowed to be in the race then.
B. She didn't think she would finish the race.
C. No one thought she would ever win.
D. She didn't want her friends to know she was running.

24. What effect do you think meeting Nanna will have on Jamey?
A. She will like Kayrn more as a friend.
B. She will want to enter the Boston Marathon.
C. She will appreciate being able to play sports.
D. She will come back to the track more often.

Diagnostic Test
Reading Comprehension
Evaluating Text

Directions for all questions in this test:

Read each passage and answer the questions that follow it. Some items will have no passage. On the answer sheet, fill in the bubble for the answer you think is correct.

Sample questions:

Many people believe that Nancy Lopez made women's professional golf the popular sport it is today. She was Rookie of the Year on the LPGA (Ladies Professional Golf Association) Tour in 1977. The next year, she won the LPGA Championship, her first major victory. She was also the leading money-winner that year. She won many more tournaments in the following years and was known as a fierce competitor. She was elected to the LPGA Hall of Fame in 1987.

---

1. Which of these is an opinion from the story?
   A. Nancy Lopez was elected to the Hall of Fame in 1987.
   B. Nancy Lopez made women's golf a popular sport.
   C. Nancy Lopez was Rookie of the Year on the LPGA Tour.
   D. Nancy Lopez won the LPGA Championship in 1978.

2. Which of these statements about golf is most believable?
   A. Many people enjoy playing golf.
   B. Almost everyone wants to be a good golfer.
   C. Golf requires more concentration than any other sport.
   D. Golfers aren't usually good at other sports.

1. Juana is writing a report about the planet Jupiter. She is using an encyclopedia as one of her reference sources. Which of these reading strategies should she use?
   A. She should just skim the encyclopedia entry and look for interesting ideas about Jupiter.
   B. She should read the first sentence of each paragraph.
   C. She should skim the encyclopedia entry and look for the key word "Jupiter."
   D. She should read slowly and carefully so she doesn't make a mistake with facts.

2. Albert heard there is an interesting article in the newspaper about his school. He wants to know if any of his friends from school are mentioned in the article. Which of these reading strategies should he use?
   A. He should skim the article and look for the key word "school."
   B. He should skim the article and look for peoples' names.
   C. He should read the article slowly and take good notes.
   D. He should read the article one paragraph at a time and compare each paragraph to a list of his friends from school.

3. Suppose you were asked by your teacher to read a two-page story about scuba diving and make a one-minute report to your class. Which of these reading strategies should you use?
   A. Skim the story and try to remember the most important ideas.
   B. Read slowly and try to memorize the whole story.
   C. Read the first and last line of each paragraph in the story.
   D. Compare the information in the story to another source, like an encyclopedia.

Rebecca moved around in her seat nervously. Her teacher had asked the students to give oral reports on family history. All the students had wonderful stories. Robbie said his great-grandfather had been a cowboy. Angelica's ancestors had come from Africa and had once been slaves. She showed a document that had given one member of her family her freedom more than a century ago.

When her turn came, Rebecca rose slowly and walked to the front of the class. She took a deep breath and began. "My family is from Germany," she started. "They were Jewish, and in the 1930s, it was a bad time in Europe. Adolph Hitler and the Nazis were rounding up Jews and putting them in work camps."

She told of how her great-grandparents decided to flee to America. "They had to walk to the border," Rebecca said. "It was more than a hundred miles. They traveled at night and slept during the day. Some kind people helped them, but it was still hard."

Rebecca held up a tiny doll. "My grandmother carried this in her pocket for weeks. It's still dirty from the trip because my grandmother never washed it. She said that it reminded her of the journey and how much people will endure for freedom."

The class was silent for a moment, then the students burst out with questions about Rebecca's story and her family. At that moment, the butterflies in Rebecca's stomach were replaced with a glow of pride. The teacher's encouraging smile told her that she had helped her classmates learn about a courageous family, her family.

4. What is this story mostly about?
  A. a teacher who asks her students to give reports
  B. a girl who tells how her family came to America
  C. a class of students who have nice stories
  D. why some people tried to escape from the Nazis

5. What is the main idea of the last paragraph?
  A. The teacher decided that Rebecca needed help.
  B. The class didn't understand Rebecca's story.
  C. Students often ask too many questions about families.
  D. Rebecca changed from being afraid to feeling proud.

6. Which of these do you learn in the first paragraph?
  A. All the students have interesting stories.
  B. Rebecca's family came from Germany.
  C. The doll was important to Rebecca's grandmother.
  D. Freedom is something worth struggling for.

Batu ran through the marketplace breathing hard. Something was going to happen at the court of his uncle, the great Khan. He wanted to be there to see it.

The boy soon arrived at the grand palace. Batu found his uncle in a small sitting room. The Khan was lying on a pile of silk pillows.

"My excited nephew, tell me what is going on," he said.

"Strangers!" Batu sputtered. "They are coming to the palace!"

The Khan's eyes lit up. "Ah, Niccolo and Maffeo Polo, they have indeed returned!"

The Khan clapped his hands. At once, the room filled with servants and guards. "Prepare for my guests," he commanded. The Khan moved to a throne at the far end of the room. Batu waited breathlessly beside him.

The doors to the room opened, and a large group entered. At the front of the group were three men. Two of them were older, but the third was young and handsome. They approached the Khan and bowed in respect.

"Oh great friend and ruler, Kublai Khan, we greet you once again," Maffeo said.

"It has been many years, my friends," the Khan said. "I welcome you with joy! Who is that young and handsome young man?"

"Your majesty," replied Niccolo, "this is my son and your servant, Marco Polo."

The great Khan said, "He is welcome and it pleases me much. This is my eager nephew, Batu." The Khan smiled. "He will be your guide while you stay in my lands. May you have many adventures and much happiness."

7. What is this story mostly about?
  A. A great ruler shows he can be kind.
  B. Some strangers come to a town far from their home.
  C. A young boy meets some travelers to his country.
  D. Friends come back to a place they had been before.

8. If this story continued, which of these would probably be the main idea of the rest of the story?
  A. Batu guides the strangers and becomes friends with Marco Polo.
  B. The strangers soon go back to where they came from.
  C. The great Khan learns who told Batu about the strangers.
  D. The reason that Kublai Khan became the ruler of the country is discussed.

9. What important idea is shown by the words from the story, ". . . we greet you once again . . ."?
  A. The travelers had come from far away.
  B. Marco was in the marketplace with Batu.
  C. Batu and Marco are old friends.
  D. Niccolo and Maffei had visited the place before.

The snow had been falling for hours. The roads were covered, and almost no cars were on the roads. Inside the house, the Lyons family was worried. The snow had knocked the telephone lines down, so they couldn't call for information. They were supposed to go to the airport today and begin their vacation. "I think the roads are too bad," said Mrs. Lyons. "We should probably do the sensible thing."

10. What sensible thing will the Lyons family probably do?
A. drive to the airport slowly because the roads are covered
B. wait until the storm has ended to start their vacation
C. call a taxi and have the driver take them to the airport
D. walk to the airport and carry their suitcases

The hikers were getting close to the top of the mountain. They would set up camp there and spend the night. The next morning, they would hike back down to the parking area. The hikers carried supplies for themselves. They also carried things the group would share, like tents, food, and things for cooking. All of the members of the group had spent a great deal of time thinking about what they would need. They wanted this hike to be challenging but not dangerous.

11. How do you know the hikers expect to have a safe trip?
A. They were not far from the parking area.
B. They were getting close to the top of the mountain.
C. They had spent a lot of time preparing for the trip.
D. They knew the trip would be challenging.

Annie closed her book with a thump. She had finished studying for her test and felt sure she would do well. All year, her grades had been improving. Annie had started the year with a bad attitude about science, and her grades had been awful. Her teacher and her parents had encouraged her, however, and now she was among the top students. The final test was tomorrow, and she felt confident.

12. What makes Annie think she will do well on the final test?
A. She had studied hard and her grades had been improving.
B. She had started the year with a bad attitude about science.
C. Her grades had been awful at the beginning of the year.
D. Other students had studied hard for the test, too.

When you watch a cartoon, you are watching something called animation. Animation is a way to make films. With animation, a filmmaker takes pictures of a series of objects or drawings. These objects or drawings change just a little bit in each photograph. Each photo is one tiny frame, or piece of film. The frames of film are then run through a projector. When the frames are shown one after the other, the objects or drawings appear to move.

Animation was first used with toys in the 1800s. One of these toys was called the zoetrope, or wheel of life. You put a long paper strip covered with drawings into the zoetrope's viewing tube. You then peered through slots, twirled the tube, and watched the drawings move. This toy led to the first animated films.

One of the earliest animated films was made with matchsticks. When this amusing 1899 film was finished, the matchsticks appeared to move around all by themselves. Later, drawings were photographed for animation. James Blackton, an American who drew for newspapers, was the first to film drawings frame by frame. This happened in 1906.

In the 1920s, the Russians made animation with puppets. The Germans created animated films using dark shapes. Other countries experimented with frame-by-frame photographs of clay figures.

In the late 1920s, Walt Disney came on the scene. Disney created some of the best-loved animated movies of all time with Mickey Mouse, Donald Duck, Goofy, and Pluto.

13. Which of these is a fact about the zoetrope?
    A. It was the first animated film.
    B. It wasn't very much fun to watch.
    C. It was a toy that led to animation.
    D. It had a strange name.

14. Which of these is a fact from the story, not an opinion?
    A. The German animations were probably too dark to see.
    B. Clay figures can be used to make animated films.
    C. The 1899 matchstick film was amusing.
    D. Most animated films are meant to be funny.

15. Which of the following is an opinion, not a fact?
    A. The Russians used puppets for their animation.
    B. James Blackton was the first to film drawings.
    C. Animation is a kind of filmmaking.
    D. Disney created the best-loved animation.

Jill looked at the clock and groaned. What was that awful hammering sound? It was only eight o'clock on a Saturday morning. She crawled out of bed and peeked outside. Seeing nothing, she closed the window with a thud. After snuggling back under the covers, the noise was still too loud. Jill buried her head under her pillow and tried to go back to sleep.

16. What caused Jill to close the window?
   A. Her room had gotten too cold.
   B. The sun was shining in her eyes.
   C. She was bothered by a noise outside.
   D. The traffic outside was too loud.

Max asked his mother if he could run with her in the mornings. Max's mother was eager for a running partner, so she said yes. On Sunday, the two went for a short run. Max was surprised when his mother said they had to do some warm-up stretches first. She explained that their leg muscles might get sore if they didn't do the stretches. After they stretched, Max said his legs felt looser and he would be able to run better.

17. What was the effect of stretching?
   A. They were able to run farther.
   B. Max's mother had a sore leg.
   C. Both of them ran faster.
   D. Max's legs felt looser.

Mail in the American Colonies was not what you might think. In 1753, Benjamin Franklin was put in charge of the postal service. He worked hard to improve everything. Even so, many people chose not to use the mail service. They believed it cost far too much. These people paid private carriers to bring their letters from place to place.

18. Why did the colonists hire their own mail carriers?
   A. They were worried about people reading their mail.
   B. They knew the carriers would get there more quickly.
   C. They thought the postal service charged too much.
   D. They did not trust Benjamin Franklin to do a good job.

The Grizzlies will be the best team in the league this year. Last year, the Grizzlies won eight games and lost only one. This year they should go undefeated. If they work hard in practice and listen to their coach, the Grizzlies should be this year's league champions.

19. Which of these is a fact from the paragraph?
 A. The Grizzlies always listen to their coach.
 B. The Grizzlies were undefeated last year.
 C. The Grizzlies will be the league champions.
 D. The Grizzlies won eight games last year.

Movie Mania wants to build a superstore in the Irvington neighborhood. The store will serve about 450 customers each day. Some people are happy because the Movie Mania store will provide jobs and convenient shopping. Others object because the store will draw so much traffic into what has been a quiet area. Some Irvington businesses believe the Movie Mania superstore will put them out of business.

20. People believe the Movie Mania store will create a traffic problem because the store will
 A. provide jobs.
 B. attract customers.
 C. be convenient.
 D. close businesses.

With only a few millimeters of rainfall each year, Peru's coast is one of the driest places on Earth. Although it borders the Amazon rain forest and the deep waters of the Pacific Ocean, the coast itself is dry and dusty. Because of the lack of water, the depressing landscape is almost empty of life.

21. Which of these is an opinion in the paragraph?
 A. The depressing landscape is almost empty of life.
 B. Peru's coast has only a few millimeters of rainfall each year.
 C. The coast itself is dry and dusty.
 D. The coast borders the Amazon rain forest.

Encyclopedia Entry

The word *sabotage* comes from the French word sabot. A sabot is a wooden shoe. The commonly accepted origin, or history, of this word is as follows: During the Industrial Revolution, French factory workers became concerned about their future. They were worried about the possibility of losing their jobs because of new automated machinery. To avoid this possibility, the workers threw their wooden shoes into their machines so they would break down. To throw a wooden shoe into a machine became sabotage, or the act of destroying property or plans on purpose. A saboteur is someone who causes sabotage.

Dictionary Entry

sab-o-tage (sab' e tazh) *n.* 1. any interference with production work in a plant or factory, especially by enemy agents or employees during a work dispute 2. any undermining of a cause *v.* to injure or attack by sabotage

History Book

Sabotage is considered by many to be one of the most terrible crimes. The act of sabotage is sneaky at best. At worst, it makes the person committing the crime a traitor. Although it was given its name during the Industrial Revolution, sabotage has been with us for thousands of years. It is likely that enslaved workers in Roman and Egyptian times used sabotage at least occasionally. In more modern times, sabotage has been a tool of warfare. It is hated by the side against whom the sabotage is committed. The side that caused the sabotage, however, sees it as a noble act.

22. Which information source gives the most complete information about sabotage?
    A. the encyclopedia
    B. the dictionary
    C. the history book
    D. They all give about the same information.

23. Which of these best describes the history book description of sabotage?
    A. It is mostly fact.
    B. It contains a lot of opinion.
    C. It shows that sabotage is usually good.
    D. It is easier to understand than the other sources.

24. If you were writing a report for school, why would the information in the encyclopedia be most useful?
    A. It is long, and long things are usually better.
    B. It goes farther back in history than the other sources.
    C. It uses a French word.
    D. It is factual, and most people would believe it.

Nubia was a kingdom in ancient Africa that extended along the Nile River from the southern boundary of ancient Egypt almost to what is today Khartoum, a city in Sudan. The Egyptians ruled Nubia for a time, getting gold there and trading for cattle, ivory, and slaves. Egypt controlled Nubia from about 2000 to 1000 B.C. Ironically the most important of Nubian civilizations, a civilization called Kush, turned the tables and ruled Egypt from about 750 to 670 B.C.

25. Which of these statements is supported by the paragraph?
    A. Egypt ruled all the countries around it for all of its history.
    B. The Egyptians made slaves of all the Nubians.
    C. Nubia was ruled by Egypt, but it also ruled Egypt for a time.
    D. Kush defeated both Egypt and Nubia around 750 B.C.

One of the most breathtaking places in the world, the Grand Canyon, lies in northwestern Arizona. It is about 277 miles long, 1 mile deep, and anywhere from 1 to 18 miles wide. The Colorado River flows along the bottom of the canyon. This river cut the rocky canyon over millions of years. In 1869, an American geologist named John Wesley Powell led a river expedition through the canyons of the Green and Colorado Rivers. Powell named the area the Grand Canyon, and his exploration of the area was one of the greatest adventures in American history. Few people remember Powell today, but he and his fellow explorers accomplished an extraordinary feat that would be difficult even with today's technology.

26. After reading this paragraph, Connie thought that a trip through the Grand Canyon would be harder than she first thought. Which words from the story caused her to think this?
    A. ". . . feat that would be difficult even with today's technology."
    B. "One of the most breathtaking places in the world . . ."
    C. "The Colorado River flows along the bottom of the canyon."
    D. ". . . Powell led a river expedition through the canyon . . ."

India's Taj Mahal is one of the most beautiful tombs ever built. The Indian ruler Shah Jahan had it built after his favorite wife, Mumtaz Mahal, died in 1629. Twenty thousand workers were needed to build the tomb, and even so, it took twenty years to complete. The tomb is made of white marble and sits on a platform of red sandstone. At each corner, there is a prayer tower. A huge dome tops the central building. Words from the Koran, the Muslim holy book, decorate the walls of the tomb. The Taj Mahal is considered one of the wonders of the modern world.

27. What can you conclude about the Taj Mahal and support with evidence from the paragraph?
    A. It was the most important building of its time.
    B. Nothing since 1629 has been more beautiful than the Taj Majal.
    C. Shah Jahan visited the Taj Mahal often after it was finished.
    D. It took a great deal of effort to complete.

Discount Auto is announcing an unusual sale. All the new cars on its lot will be sold at the amazing price of $1,000. These cars normally sell for $10,000 to $20,000, so this is a once-in-a-lifetime opportunity. This is a first-come, first-served sale, so get there early. The price of the cars includes taxes and all other costs. Bring your checkbook and drive away in the car of your dreams.

28. Why is this announcement not very believable?
   A. It doesn't tell you what color the cars are.
   B. The sale price of the cars is much too low.
   C. It doesn't ask people how much money they have.
   D. The normal price of the cars is much too low.

Scientists have found an orbiting object beyond the planet Pluto. Some people think this might be a tenth planet, but they are not sure. Others believe it is an asteroid, an object that is orbiting the sun but is too small to be a planet. It will be difficult to resolve this difference of opinion. The object is extremely far from Earth and is hard to observe, even with a powerful telescope. This new object has not been named yet.

29. Which of these statements about the passage is most likely to be true?
   A. A new object has been found beyond Pluto.
   B. The new object is a planet.
   C. The new object is an asteroid.
   D. You can see the object on a clear night.

Mr. and Mrs. Jackson are hoping to complete a marathon this summer. A marathon is a running race that is more than 26 miles long. Some people consider it one of the most difficult athletic competitions. The Jacksons have been training for almost a year, and they believe they will finish the race. They have gradually increased the distance they run and have competed in some shorter races.

30. Which statement from the paragraph leads you to believe the Jacksons will finish the race?
   A. They are hoping to complete the race.
   B. People think marathons are difficult.
   C. A marathon is more than 26 miles long.
   D. They have been training for almost a year.

Many children today attend Montessori schools. These schools are named after a woman named Maria Montessori. Montessori became famous for creating a special way of teaching.

In 1896, Montessori's future looked bright. She had graduated from the university in Rome as the first Italian woman to get a medical degree. She took a job working with children who had trouble learning. People did not think these children could learn, but Montessori disagreed. She worked very hard to develop a new way of teaching. To everyone's surprise, Montessori's students did learn.

With this success behind her, Montessori decided to start her own school. Her first school opened in 1907. Montessori's new students were preschool children from poor families. These students, too, learned quickly. Special materials helped them become confident and independent learners. The young students studied life around them through touch, sight, hearing, smell, and taste. Older students learned to think creatively using their imagination. Students of different ages worked together in groups. Later, they reported what they had learned to the rest of the class.

Montessori believed her new way of teaching was important. She traveled and gave talks on her teaching style. She also wrote books about it.

Today, Montessori schools can be found all over the world. Teachers are still being trained to teach the Maria Montessori way, and children are still learning because of her.

31. Maria Montessori believed that
   A. children should take lots of tests.
   B. painting was just like writing.
   C. she was the world's best teacher.
   D. all children were able to learn.

32. Montessori's teaching style was so successful that
   A. she started opening up her own universities.
   B. schools in other places began teaching her way.
   C. many of her students grew up to become teachers.
   D. parents of her students began attending classes.

33. Why did Maria Montessori open her own school?
   A. She wanted to teach wealthy students.
   B. She got fired from her old job.
   C. She wanted to do things her way.
   D. She liked going to medical school.

The city of Clarksdale needs a new baseball field. Though the field we use now is only five years old, the field is impossible to play on. The city planted new grass last year after a rainy season. Every week, before the games, the grass is mowed. The teams that use the field are not allowed to practice on the field. Though these things have helped, the field needs to be replaced.

34. In the passage, the author says Clarksdale's baseball field is impossible to play on. How does the author support this statement?
   A. Every week, before the games, the grass is mowed.
   B. The city of Clarksdale needs a new baseball field.
   C. All the city teams practice on the field during the week.
   D. The author does not support this inference in the passage.

Art Riley was overweight. He did everything he could to eat better, but nothing seemed to work. Then Art discovered Tully Snead's low-fat menu. He found great-tasting foods that he liked. Art was a new man. He ate at Tully Snead's Restaurant every night, and six months later he was sixty pounds lighter! It's hard to find restaurants that care about your health. We have found a way to make food fast, fresh, and low in fat. Come try our low-fat menu and watch the pounds come off.

35. Which of these is an example of incorrect thinking, based on the information in the story?
   A. Eating foods low in fat helped Art Riley lose weight.
   B. Eating at Tully Snead's will cause people to lose weight.
   C. Art Riley likes Tully Snead's low-fat menu.
   D. Tully Snead's Restaurant has a low-fat menu.

The Martin Construction Co. wants to buy an acre of land on the corner of Butler and Fifth Street and build a parking lot. The land is next to Jackson Elementary School and in front of the Oak Meadow neighborhood. This community should not allow a parking lot to be built on public land. Building a parking lot will increase the noise in the neighborhood. Trees will have to be cut down. Play areas for children and families will be lost. We cannot sit by and watch part of our neighborhood become a parking lot. The money gained for the community is not worth the price of our trees and play areas. I ask the Council to look at the facts and do the right thing.

36. Which of these is an example of persuasion from the passage?
   A. The parking lot will be built next to Jackson Elementary School.
   B. Martin Construction Co. wants to buy land to build a parking lot.
   C. Martin Construction Co. is greedy and wants to ruin the community.
   D. The money gained is not worth the loss of the trees and play areas.

The elephant is the largest animal on Earth. A mature African elephant can weigh as much as 15,000 pounds and stand over 13 feet tall. To support this huge size, elephants may eat as much as 500 pounds of plant matter a day. To wash it down, an elephant can drink 50 gallons or more of water. No other animal even comes close to an elephant's size.

37. Why is the author's statement that the elephant is the largest animal on Earth wrong?
   A. The author doesn't say exactly how big a mature elephant is.
   B. The author doesn't mention that there are two kinds of elephants, African and Indian.
   C. The author doesn't mention whales, which are larger than elephants.
   D. The author doesn't say how long an elephant can live.

Historians believe that Franklin Delano Roosevelt was among the greatest American presidents. During his terms of office, Roosevelt successfully faced two enormous challenges, the Great Depression and World War II. His ability to deal with these events was recognized by the voters. He won the presidency four times, a feat that no previous president had ever accomplished. FDR, as he was known, was confined to a wheelchair because of polio, but this disability did nothing to hinder his effectiveness as president.

38. Which of these is the most important evidence that Franklin Delano Roosevelt was a great president?
   A. He successfully faced two enormous challenges.
   B. Historians believe he was a great president.
   C. He was successful even though he was in a wheelchair.
   D. He served 16 years as president.

The Sahara is the largest desert in the world. Located in northern Africa, it covers more than three million square miles. It is one of the most difficult places on Earth in which to live.

39. Which of these is the best support for the opinion that the Sahara is one of the most difficult places on Earth in which to live?
   A. Natural and artificial oases in the desert allow some plants to live in a relatively small area.
   B. Surprisingly, the Sahara has become economically important because of oil wells in the northern desert.
   C. Some of the desert is below sea level, but some of it rises more than 1600 feet above sea level.
   D. Almost no rain falls there, and the temperatures range from below freezing to more than 130° F.

The community of Fernwood should reject the plan to build a Handy Supply at 42nd Place and Halsey. A business like this will certainly hurt our community.

Although Handy Supply says it will be a pedestrian-friendly business, this is not the case. It's true that a person could walk to the Handy Supply to pick up a hammer and nails. The average customer, however, will more likely drive an automobile there.

When this was pointed out to Handy Supply, the company had a quick reply. They said Fernwood's Handy Supply would provide more home delivery than other branches. Although this may cut down on single-car traffic, it will only increase truck traffic on our already crowded streets.

Developers say that the Handy Supply's large parking lot will "add to Fernwood's community feeling" by encouraging more bicyclists, walkers, and shoppers. I fail to see how a parking lot can inspire such activities.

The Handy Supply will supposedly bring life to local businesses. In truth, huge national stores such as Handy Supply hurt other businesses. Because of Handy Supply's size, it can give customers a larger selection of goods as well as cheaper prices. This leads to a loss of customers at smaller stores.

Handy Supply has made a lot of promises it cannot keep. Such a large parking-lot style business can in no way be pedestrian-friendly, encourage community feeling, and bring life to other businesses. A community like Fernwood should know better than to believe everything it hears.

40. Which of the author's arguments against the Handy Supply is the strongest?
   A. The store will provide more delivery services.
   B. The store will hurt other businesses.
   C. The store will increase traffic congestion.
   D. The store will be at an already busy intersection.

41. Which argument against the Handy Supply does the author present first?
   A. The store will not be pedestrian-friendly.
   B. The store will increase truck traffic.
   C. The store will hurt the smaller businesses.
   D. The store will not cut down on traffic.

42. How does the author tie all of the arguments against Handy Supply together?
   A. by talking about them one at a time
   B. by starting off with a warning
   C. by repeating them at the end
   D. by saying Fernwood should know better

I believe that school uniforms are an all-around good idea. When students at our school started wearing uniforms, there was an immediate reaction. Student behavior began to change—for the better. There were fewer classroom interruptions and hallway disturbances. Students seemed to care less about what they were wearing and more about what they were learning. Only one year after the school adopted uniforms, test scores improved by 15 percent.

43. Which of the following is the weakest support for the belief that school uniforms are a good idea?
   A. Students test scores improved.
   B. There were fewer classroom interruptions.
   C. There were fewer disturbances in the halls.
   D. Students cared less about what they wore.

Even though Rose City Park is a place where dogs are allowed to be off their leashes, I think dogs should be kept on leashes at all times. I like dogs, and the dogs I have met at Rose City have been friendly; but the problem is, you can never tell when someone may bring a dangerous dog to the park. Besides, dogs don't need to be off their leashes to get enough exercise. Dog owners just need to be willing to walk farther and more often. The only place a dog should be let off its leash is in its own backyard.

44. How does the author support the argument that dogs should be kept on leashes?
   A. Dogs at the park are sometimes unfriendly.
   B. Owners should walk dogs farther.
   C. Dogs without leashes belong in a yard.
   D. The author does not support the argument.

Starting today, Olsen's Market asks that no one under the age of 16 sit on the benches outside of the market. If you wish to buy something here, please come inside and do so. If you have already bought something, please find another place to spend your time. Youngsters sitting outside the market all day is bad for our business. Our older customers need a place to sit and visit with each other.

45. There is enough information in this passage to show that
   A. Olsen's likes older customers more than younger ones.
   B. Olsen's younger customers have been causing trouble.
   C. Olsen's is tired of finding trash around the benches.
   D. Olsen's wants the younger customers to spend more money.

Diagnostic Test
Reading Comprehension
Locating and Using Information

Directions for all questions in this test:

Read each passage and answer the questions that follow it. Some items will have no passage. On the answer sheet, fill in the bubble for the answer you think is correct.

Sample questions:

> (1) In geology, a fault is a crack or fracture in Earth's crust. (2) The sections of rock on either side of the fault often move. (3) When the movement is quick, an earthquake takes place. (4) When the movement is slow, it is rarely noticed. (5) Over time, however, even slight movements may change the land considerably. (6) The Wasatch Range of mountains in Utah, which are over 10,000 feet high, were created by slow movements of a fault over many thousands of years.

1. Which sentence tells how an earthquake is caused?
   A. Sentence 1
   B. Sentence 2
   C. Sentence 3
   D. Sentence 4

2. If you were taking notes about this paragraph, which of these would be most important?
   A. Earthquakes take place.
   B. A fault is a crack in Earth's crust.
   C. Slow movements are rarely noticed.
   D. The Wasatch Range is in Utah.

The broadband high-speed modem is compatible with both Macintosh and PC computers. It has been designed to install easily, and we are confident it will give you years of service.

To begin, open the box and follow the directions on the lid to remove the modem. Do not throw the box and packing materials away. If you ever have to transport the modem, you can repack it so it won't be damaged in the move. The box and packing materials will also come in handy if you ever have to return the modem for service or an upgrade.

Compare the contents of the box with the parts and assembly sheet. Make sure you have all the parts. If you are missing a part, call our customer service number (800/555-1256).

Plug one end of the gray power cord into the modem and the other end into an electrical outlet. This step is important in order to discharge any static electricity. Connect one end of the blue telephone cable to the modem. The correct port on the modem is labeled with the words PHONE LINE IN. Connect the other end of the cable to a nearby telephone outlet.

If you wish to share the telephone line with a voice phone, simply connect the cable from the phone to the port labeled CONNECT TELEPHONE HERE. You will be able to use the phone just as if it were connected to the wall telephone outlet.

The next step is to connect the modem to the computer. If you are using a PC, choose the white cable. If you are using a Macintosh, choose the black cable. Connect one end of the computer to the port of your computer labeled MODEM or TELEPHONE. Connect the other end to the modem port labeled CONNECT COMPUTER CABLE HERE.

1. What color cable would you use to connect the modem to a Macintosh computer?
   A. black
   B. white
   C. blue
   D. gray

2. Which cable should you connect right after the power cable?
   A. the cable from the modem to the printer
   B. the cable from the computer to the modem
   C. the cable from a phone to the modem
   D. the cable from the modem to the telephone outlet

3. Why is it important to plug the power cord into the modem and the electrical outlet?
   A. It gives you power so you can turn the modem on.
   B. It lets the modem lights go on.
   C. It prevents damage from static electricity.
   D. It tells the computer that the modem is ready.

Doggie Dash 5K and 10K Race
April 3, 9:00 AM
All proceeds from the race go to
Westside Animal Shelter

Entry Fee: $20 on or before March 27, $25 after March 27
Location: Hemingway Park

1. Name: _____

2. Address: _____

3. Telephone: _____

4. Your age on the day of the race: _____

5. Shirt size: S   M   L   XL (Circle one)

6. Gender: M   F

7. Print your name: _____

8. Signature: _____

If under 18, a parent's signature is also required.

Complete this form and mail it with a check before race day to Westside Animal Shelter, 203 Miller Avenue. The form and check may be submitted in person before 8:00 A.M. on the day of the race.

---

4. Which information goes on line 4?
  A. the year you were born
  B. how old you are on race day
  C. what grade you are in
  D. the date of your birthday

5. Where would you submit the form if it was March 20?
  A. carry it to your school
  B. carry it to the park
  C. mail it to the park
  D. mail it to the animal shelter

6. After you print your name, what do you need to do next?
  A. write your address
  B. circle your shirt size
  C. sign the form
  D. have a parent sign

These are the instructions for recording a personal greeting on your new answering machine. Your greeting may be up to two minutes long. If you do not record a personal greeting, a pre-recorded greeting will play when a call comes in.

To Record Your Greeting
1. Press the GREETING REC button to activate the answering machine.
2. Within five seconds, press the GREETING REC button again to record your greeting. (A long beep will sound.)
3. After the long beep, speak clearly, remaining about eight inches from the letters MIC. (This is the machine's microphone.)
   —The display will show how long your greeting is.
   —If you speak for over two minutes, the unit will stop recording automatically
4. Press the STOP button.
   —A long beep will sound.
   —To change the message, repeat from step 1.

Note: To check the greeting, press the GREETING CHECK button.

Greeting Suggestion:
"Hello, this is (your name). You have reached (your number). Sorry I can't take your call. Please leave a message after the beep. Thank you."

7. What should you do just before you speak into the microphone?
   A. practice your greeting
   B. listen for a long beep
   C. press the MIC button
   D. listen to the instructions

8. What does the GREETING CHECK button allow you to do?
   A. listen to your personal greeting
   B. erase a previous greeting
   C. reduce the volume of your greeting
   D. adjust the length of your greeting

9. What happens if your greeting is longer than two minutes?
   A. The message will be erased.
   B. The display light flashes.
   C. The unit gives you a warning.
   D. The machine stops recording.

James Smithson was a very wealthy man. When he died in 1829, he left his riches to the United States. Smithson was a British scientist. He wanted his fortune to help spread knowledge. In 1846, Congress used his money to build the Smithsonian.

The Smithsonian Institution is an organization of educational sites in Washington, D.C. People go to these places to learn. Many of these places are museums. There are art, history, space, and science museums.

The National Museum of American Art features different forms of art from Colonial times to today. People go there to see American crafts, portraits of famous people, and other works.

The National Museum of Natural History has exhibits on all types of living things. People who visit this museum can learn about human, animal, and plant life.

The National Museum of American History has some interesting collections. Visitors to this museum will see displays of household and military items, plus inventions from America's past. The National Air and Space Museums keep records of the United States air and space flight accomplishments and plans.

The Smithsonian is in charge of other educational sites, too. The National Zoological Park has over 2,000 mammals, birds, and reptiles. And there are Smithsonian research centers where rain forest, ocean, and space environments are studied.

Over 150 years have passed since the Smithsonian was created. In that time, James Smithson's gift has certainly achieved his goal of spreading knowledge.

10. Here is an outline of the passage.

About the Smithsonian
I. Why it was created
II. Organization
   A. Museums
      1. American Art
      2. Natural History
      3. Air and Space
   B. _____
   C. Research Centers

Which answer would fit best in the blank in the outline?
A. James Smithson
B. Congress
C. The Zoo
D. Knowledge

11. If you were taking notes about this passage, which of these would be least important?
A. Many people visit the Smithsonian.
B. James Smithson was a scientist.
C. The Museum of Natural History has exhibits on all types of living things.
D. The Smithsonian is located in Washington, D.C.

12. Which of these is the best summary of the passage?
A. Spreading knowledge is one of the jobs of the U.S. Congress.
B. The Smithsonian teaches Americans about art.
C. Research at the Smithsonian helps scientists around the world.
D. The Smithsonian is an important group of educational sites in D.C.

Diagnostic Test
Literary Response and Analysis
Structural Features

Directions for all questions in this test:

Read each passage and answer the questions that follow it. Some items will have no passage. On the answer sheet, fill in the bubble for the answer you think is correct.

Sample question:

1. A biography of Joan of Arc would be considered
   A. fiction.
   B. nonfiction.
   C. drama.
   D. poetry.

1. Which form of literature would have characters like elves, talking animals, or dwarves?
   A. historic fiction
   B. fairy tale
   C. fable
   D. autobiography

2. Which of these probably came from a fantasy story?
   A. The Grand Canyon is so amazing that it can take your breath away.
   B. The more Juan learned about his grandmother, the more amazing her life seemed.
   C. The armies of Alexander the Great conquered every enemy they met.
   D. When Kerry walked into the closet, she entered a world that was exactly like her dreams.

3. Which of these usually teaches a lesson?
   A. fable
   B. legend
   C. biography
   D. comedy

4. Which of these is true about legends?
   A. They are about people or things that never existed.
   B. They are about true events exactly as they happened.
   C. They are often partially true but exaggerated.
   D. They tell about real people who did funny things.

5. Which of these is a characteristic of poetry?
   A. Facts are presented so that you can understand them easily.
   B. The setting is described in great detail.
   C. Characters are on the stage in costume.
   D. Rhyme and rhythm help you understand the meaning.

6. What is an important goal of drama?
   A. to help the reader understand history
   B. to make the actors seem like real people
   C. to end each line with a rhyming word
   D. to describe scenery in a lot of detail

7. What is a great advantage of fiction?
   A. You can write about things that haven't happened.
   B. You always write about history or real people.
   C. You just tell facts and don't have to worry about a story.
   D. You can use rhyme to make things sound more important.

8. What is the main purpose of nonfiction?
   A. to draw the reader into the action
   B. to use words in an unusual way
   C. to share information that is true
   D. to make the audience understand characters

9. How is a legend different from a story that is pure fiction?
   A. A legend is usually a true story that has been exaggerated.
   B. A legend is longer than pure fiction.
   C. A legend always has a happy ending.
   D. A legend is about animals that behave a lot like people.

10. What is true about historic fiction?
   A. It is a true story about a person who lived long ago.
   B. It is a made-up story about something that will happen in the future.
   C. It is a true story about something that happened long ago.
   D. It is a made-up story, but it tells about real people or events.

11. Which of these best describes a folktale?
   A. It is a long story that is never written down. People gather around a fire and tell the story again and again.
   B. It is a made-up story shared by a group of people with a similar language or history. A folktale often teaches a lesson.
   C. It is a true story about something that happened long ago. A folktale has a happy ending and the lines rhyme.
   D. It is a story that is sung by a group of people on a stage. The people in the audience sometimes sing along.

12. Which of these probably came from a book of realistic fiction?
   A. When the giant saw the children, he didn't know what they were.
   B. Maria didn't want to miss the game, but she really didn't feel well.
   C. The boy stepped from behind the tree and looked up at the knight on his horse.
   D. After years of traveling through space, the explorers reached the new planet.

The Mediterranean Sea has often been called the "cradle of civilization." Many of the great civilizations of the world were born in the lands that border the Mediterranean. Even so, the title "cradle of civilization" might be an exaggeration. Other parts of the world, including southern Africa, India, China, and the Americas, also produced great civilizations.

13. This paragraph was written mostly
   A. to show that the Mediterranean is the cradle of civilization.
   B. to argue against a point of view.
   C. to entertain the reader.
   D. to tell a story about a body of water.

When Saari heard the great noise, she rushed to the doorway. A huge dragon was circling the village. Terrified people ran this way and that. Slowly, the dragon folded its wings and landed in a field at the edge of the village. Instead of destroying the houses, this dragon walked carefully between them. He headed straight toward Saari as if he had known her his whole life.

14. Which of these best describes this paragraph?
   A. It is the beginning of a story meant to persuade.
   B. It compares dragons to old friends.
   C. It is like an encyclopedia entry about dragons.
   D. It is part of a story meant to entertain the reader.

15. Which of these probably came from a book that compares life today with life long ago?
   A. The first people to come to America were probably nomads from Asia. They walked across a land bridge from Siberia to Alaska.
   B. Desert plants and animals have learned to survive in harsh conditions. They can withstand heat, cold, drought, and flood.
   C. Older residents of Los Angeles remember when much of the city was farmland. Today, these farms have been replaced with houses, shopping malls, and superhighways.
   D. Fishing has always been the favorite activity of the Montoya family. They spend almost every weekend at a lake or river, and they plan their vacations around a trip to a special fishing spot.

Diagnostic Test
Literary Response and Analysis
Narrative Analysis: Story Elements

Directions *for all questions in this test:*

Read each passage and answer the questions that follow it. Some items will have no passage. On the answer sheet, fill in the bubble for the answer you think is correct.

Sample questions:

The ship was just a few miles from shore when the storm hit. The captain wasn't sure what to do. The mouth of the harbor was narrow and rocky. A sudden wave or gust of wind could push the ship onto the rocks. If he kept the ship in the open ocean, the storm might capsize it. Neither choice was very good, but the captain had to make a decision. After considering everything, the captain decided to head into the harbor. He was confident his crew would be able to handle the challenge.

---

1. What caused the problem in this story?
  A. the captain
  B. the storm
  C. the open ocean
  D. the harbor

2. Which of these best describes the captain?
  A. angry
  B. disappointed
  C. weak
  D. able

The Celts were an ancient people who lived in Europe. They held power from about 400 B.C. until the first century A.D. During that time, the Celts were feared and respected by the rest of the world.

Women in Celtic civilization had great freedom. Some Celtic women became important warriors and queens. The most famous Celtic queen was Boudicca. She led a rebellion against Roman rule.

Boudicca, whose name means "victory," was the wife of a Celtic king named Prasutagus. Together, they ruled over a British Celtic tribe called the Iceni. The Iceni and the Romans were friends while Prasutagus was alive.

In about 60 A.D., Prasutagus died. He left half of his wealth to Rome and half to his two teenage daughters. Roman soldiers came to collect their part of what Prasutagus had left. Boudicca and the Iceni greeted them with friendship and kindness. In return, the Romans turned on the people. They took property and made some Celts their slaves. Boudicca protested this harsh treatment. The Romans attacked her and her family. Boudicca and the Iceni were furious. Boudicca led her Celtic people into war against the Romans.

At first, Boudicca and the Celts won many battles. They even destroyed the city of London, which was a Roman fortress then. Finally, however, the Romans defeated Boudicca and the Celts. No one knows exactly what happened to Boudicca. No matter what, she remains a symbol of Celtic power and freedom.

1. What is this story mostly about?
   A. ancient people who lived in Europe long ago
   B. a Celtic queen who battled the Romans
   C. why the Romans were friends with the Iceni
   D. why London became a Roman fortress

2. What was the first thing that caused a problem between the Romans and the Iceni?
   A. Prasutagus left some of his wealth to Rome.
   B. The Romans took property and made the Celts their slaves.
   C. Boudicca led her people into war against the Romans.
   D. The Romans defeated Boudicca and the Celts.

3. Which of these is not explained in the story?
   A. what made Boudicca and the Iceni angry
   B. when Prasutagus died
   C. who the Iceni were
   D. what happened to Boudicca

Spike was Jeremy's pet bird. He had a spike of yellow feathers on his head. He chirped Jeremy awake every morning.

"Hey, Spike!" Jeremy would always say.

One morning Jeremy woke up to a silent room. The door to Spike's cage was open. Spike was gone.

Jeremy looked in the closet and under the bed. No Spike. Jeremy searched through the house. Spike was nowhere to be found.

"He must have flown away," he thought sadly.

Just then, Jeremy heard a faint "chirrup" from the attic. Jeremy rushed upstairs. The attic door was open. Spike flew around the room in a burst of yellow feathers. Jeremy held out his finger and Spike landed on it.

"Hey, Spike!" Jeremy said with a smile.

4. What problem did Jeremy have in this story?
   A. Jeremy fell asleep.
   B. Spike was missing.
   C. The attic door was open.
   D. Spike kept waking Jeremy.

Bethany had so much homework. There were spelling words to learn and a report to write. She knew it would take a long time.

"I don't want to study that long," she told her dad.

Dad showed her an old wind-up clock with two big bells on the top. "This is a magic clock," he said. "It makes time seem to go faster."

That evening, Bethany set the alarm on the clock so she would have one hour to study. An hour seemed like a very long time, but she gave it a try. She started with her spelling words. When she looked up, fifteen minutes had gone by, and she had finished them! Then she wrote her book report. Soon, the alarm on the clock jangled loudly. The hour had passed much faster than Bethany thought. In fact, she was just about finished with her book report.

5. How did the clock help Bethany?
   A. It made her think about school.
   B. It went off when she made a spelling mistake.
   C. It reminded her that she had spelling words to do.
   D. It made the time seem to go by faster.

All summer Kate and her dog Buster played in the backyard. One day, Kate sat on her back porch step with Buster. School was starting the next day. Kate thought about how unhappy Buster would be in the house all day long. Then she got an idea. Kate raced to the kitchen and got a length of rope and Buster's leash. She tied one end of the rope to the back porch railing. She put the rope through the loop at the end of Buster's leash. Then, she stretched the rope across the yard and tied it to a tree. When she put Buster on the leash, he could run up and down the yard. The leash, which was attached to the rope, kept him safe.

"Now you can run and play until I come home from school!" Kate said.

Continued on page 38.

6. What problem did the rope and leash solve?
   A. letting Kate get to school faster
   B. keeping Buster off the couch
   C. exercising Buster while Kate was away
   D. telling Buster when Kate would come home

Collecting firewood was Danielle's least favorite chore. With a sigh of boredom, she picked up another small branch and tossed it on the flat wagon. Her brother, Phillipe, worked beside her. He didn't like the chore much, either.

It was late November, and the pale afternoon sun would be setting soon. Danielle's heart sank when she looked at the cold sky. The long winter months cooped up inside their small cottage in France seemed to last forever.

A strange shadow passed over the sun and Danielle looked up. For a moment all she saw was a huge, round cloud. Then, she heard her brother gasp.

"What is that?" he cried. He pointed upward to the round cloud. Danielle looked more closely; then, she gasped, too. The thing covering the sun wasn't a cloud. It was some kind of gigantic flying object! It was large and round, and a basket hung down below it.

The round object floated upward over their heads. Danielle and Phillipe watched it, their mouths open with shock. Suddenly a head popped over the edge of the basket. It was a man! He waved to them as he passed overhead. The strange object soon disappeared beyond some trees.

Danielle and her brother broke into a run. They went through the trees to their father's hay field beyond. Sure enough, the huge object had landed in the field with a bump.

"Hello, children," one of the men said. "I am Pilâtre de Rosier. You just saw the first flight of a balloon carrying people. Today, November 21, 1783, will be famous in history!"

---

7. Why did the writer begin this story by making the children seem bored?
   A. It makes France seem like a boring place.
   B. It makes the people in the balloon seem bored, too.
   C. It makes the story longer.
   D. It makes the later events seem more exciting.

8. Which words does the author use to create a sense of mystery about the balloon?
   A. "A strange shadow passed over the sun . . ."
   B. "Danielle looked more closely . . ."
   C. "Danielle and her brother broke into a run."
   D. "He waved to them . . ."

9. What is the purpose of the last paragraph of the story?
   A. It explains why balloons fly.
   B. It shows that this is a true story.
   C. It helps the reader understand France.
   D. It tells why the children were collecting firewood.

Dana wanted to go to the arts and crafts store. When her mother asked what she needed, Dana mysteriously replied, "It's a secret." Smiling, Dana's mother agreed. While Dana shopped, her mother waited in the car. She did not want to spoil the surprise.

The next day, Dana handed her mother a small box. "Open it," she said. Inside, there was a bracelet made of beads. There was also a note that said, "Happy Mother's Day, to someone who knows me too well."

10. Why did Dana's mother stay in the car?
A. She wanted to give Dana privacy.
B. She disliked arts and crafts stores.
C. She wanted to take a short nap.
D. She had just been to the store recently.

Aaron and Andrew were in the basement, going through their toy collection. The summer garage sale was coming up, and they wanted to make some money. After working all morning, the boys had divided everything into two piles. One pile contained toys that were still special to them. The other pile, which was much larger, was made up of toys they were willing to part with. Bounding up the stairs, the boys announced that they were done. "Oh, no," their father said. "Now you have to put a price on each toy."

11. Why did the boys make two piles of toys?
A. One was for Aaron, and the other was for Andrew.
B. The two piles were going to be priced differently.
C. The boys were selling only some of their toys.
D. One pile was worth more money than the other.

Jake has an unusual job. He is a cook for a crew of five on a tugboat. People always ask what it's like to cook at sea. He says it depends on the weather. On calm days, cooking is a breeze. But when the seas become violent, and the boat is tossed up and down and side to side, cooking can be a challenge. One of Jake's tricks is to put a bunch of rolled-up tin foil on either side of a baking dish while it's in the oven. He also uses recipes that will turn out, even when there is a lot of movement.

12. Why does Jake put foil around a baking dish during a storm?
A. to keep it from moving around
B. to help it cook without heat
C. to help it stay nice and fresh
D. to keep it away from the crew

Read these three stories and then answer the questions about them.

A father died and left his only son one hundred dirhams. The son bought glassware with his money. He hoped to resell the glass and make more money.

He thought, "This glass will sell for two hundred dirhams. I can use it to buy more glass and more things to sell. Soon I will have thousands of dirhams. I will buy a fine house and marry the sultan's daughter. I will wear fine silks and be a powerful man. People will be jealous of my wealth and fame. I will shake my fist at them!"

The son shook his fist, knocking the glass to the ground where it shattered. He lost his glassware and his dream.

A farmer's daughter had milked the cows. As she returned home, the milkmaid began daydreaming. "I can get cream from the milk in my pail. I will make butter from the cream and sell it. I will buy eggs, which will hatch into chickens. Soon, I will sell the chickens and use the money to buy a new gown. I will be so pretty that the handsome prince will marry me. I will live in the castle forever."

The farmer's daughter was too busy daydreaming to watch where she was going. She tripped on a rock and dropped her pail in the dirt. Her milk, and her dreams, spilled onto the road.

Once a boy was walking through the forest. He spied a fox through the trees. The fox was fast asleep. The boy got very excited.

"I could trap the fox and sell it in the market," he thought. "I will use the money to buy seeds to grow a great garden. People will see my garden and be very jealous. They will want to steal the vegetables in the garden. If they do, I will shout at them, 'Get out of my garden!'"

The boy shouted so loudly that the fox woke up. It raced into the forest. The boy lost his fox and his great garden.

13. Which lesson is contained in all of these stories?
   A. It's better to work slowly and not make mistakes.
   B. Dreams almost never come true.
   C. Old dogs can learn new tricks.
   D. Don't count on something until you have it.

14. How are all three characters alike?
   A. They all had plans that helped other people.
   B. They all lost what they had because of other people.
   C. They all made a mistake that ruined their plans.
   D. They all ended up with more than they started.

15. In which way is the third story different from the others?
   A. The boy never really had anything, but the son and the milkmaid did.
   B. The boy wanted to use his money to do something that would help others.
   C. The boy almost had his garden.
   D. The boy planned better than the others.

Isaac was bored. Mom was working in her office, and his sister Joan was upstairs frantically looking for something to wear for some silly date. Isaac sighed and flipped channels on the television in the living room.

Joan pounded down the stairs. "Let's go," she said.

"Where are we going?" Isaac asked.

"Shopping," Joan said.

Isaac's heart sank. "No way," he said.

"I can't leave you home alone," Joan said.

Soon, they were in the old section of town. Joan parked in front of a plain brick building.

"This isn't the mall," Isaac said.

"It's a thrift store," Joan said.

Inside, the store smelled like mothballs and musty clothes. An older woman sat on a stool, watching a small television.

While Joan tried on dresses, Isaac looked around. Old clothes filled every spare inch of space. After a few minutes of poking around, he found boxes of old shoes. He pulled out a pair of old army boots that were faded and worn. Some of the kids at school were wearing boots, but no one had any that looked like this.

He tried on the boots. They fit perfectly. Soon, Joan came out of the dressing room. She was wearing a great dress, and she was in a much better mood than before. Joan looked down at Isaac's feet and saw the shoes. She smiled. "Okay, you've been a good sport. I'll buy them for you."

Isaac looked at his feet and grinned. He couldn't wait to tell his friends about his strange shopping adventure and the perfect pair of shoes.

16. Why did Joan "pound" down the stairs?
  A. She felt she didn't have the right thing to wear on a date.
  B. She was annoyed that she had to watch Isaac.
  C. She wanted to shop at the mall, not a thrift store.
  D. She wanted Isaac to stop flipping the television channels.

17. Which of these is probably true about Isaac?
  A. He would rather watch television than play sports.
  B. He complains until his sister buys him something.
  C. He seems to be easily satisfied.
  D. He likes to boast about all the things he has.

18. What can you say about Joan at the end of the story?
  A. She wishes she had found boots like the ones Isaac found.
  B. She thought she looked good in the dress she had bought.
  C. She thought Isaac looked silly in the boots he wanted.
  D. She doesn't really look as good as she thinks she does.

For years, the huge old Andrews place sat empty in a weedy lot. It had once been a grand home, but now, it was a wreck. The Main Street Historical Society wanted to turn the house into a museum. They held bake sales and flea markets to raise money, but still didn't have enough. The Society wrote to the newspaper asking for help.

The next meeting of the Historical Society was packed with people. Maddie Rose, the society's president, was surprised. The room was filled with kids! Most society members were older, and many of them were grandparents. They had never seen kids at their meetings before.

When the meeting started, a smiling young girl stood up. "My name is Sarah Wilson, and these are my friends," she said. "We are in sixth grade and saw your letter in the newspaper. We've been studying city history in class. We would like to help you fix the Andrews House."

Many society members were against the idea. They didn't believe that a bunch of kids could be any help. One member, Fred Thompson, was especially against the idea. Over his objections, the Society agreed to let the kids help.

The next Saturday was clean-up day at the Andrews House. Maddie arrived early. The place was swarming with kids and Society members. Together, they were pulling out the weeds, raking the yard, and hauling away trash. The place buzzed with activity, and everyone seemed to be having a good time.

Fred saw Maddie and walked over to her. He said sheepishly, "I never would have believed that kids could do this much good."

Maddie smiled. She knew better. "Now what do you think of kids helping out?"

19. Which of these is probably true about Sarah?
   A. She was against the idea of helping at first.
   B. She probably helped organize the students.
   C. She never helped out like this before.
   D. She didn't really like Fred Thompson.

20. At the end of the story, Fred Thompson
   A. was pleased at what the students were doing.
   B. still didn't want the help of the students.
   C. thought fixing the house was a waste of time.
   D. was working harder than anyone else.

21. On Saturday, it appears as if
   A. Maddie Rose was working less than she thought.
   B. the students had raised a lot of money.
   C. Sarah had changed her mind about Mr. Thompson.
   D. most Society members enjoyed working with the students.

Most of the kids in Ricardo's class loved sports. Everyone played touch football and basketball. In spring, everyone played baseball in the vacant lot down the street.

Watching other kids play sports saddened Ricardo. It wasn't that he didn't like sports. It was just that Ricardo wasn't very good at sports.

One day, he went with his brother, Juan, to soccer practice. Juan was one of the best soccer players in the city league.

"So why aren't I good at something?" Ricardo said as they drove to the soccer field. "Maybe I'll never be good at any sport."

Juan grinned at his little brother. "You just haven't found your sport yet. When you do, you'll know."

While Juan was at practice, Ricardo got bored. He tossed a few baskets on the basketball court next to the field. Then, he spied an archery range. An older girl was shooting arrows at the target. Ricardo went to watch her.

"Hey, you're pretty good," Ricardo said.

"Thanks," the girl said. "You want to try it?"

She showed Ricardo how to hold a bow and to pull the bowstring. She explained how to line up the arrow with the target. The bow felt comfortable in Ricardo's hands. The arrow seemed to line up on the target all by itself. He let the arrow fly.

"Thwack!" The arrow hit the target close to the center. "That was great!" the girl said. "You sure you've never done this before?"

Ricardo looked at the arrow vibrating slightly in the target. Shooting was easy, and it felt good to hit the target. Maybe this was what Juan was talking about.

Ricardo grinned. "No," he said. "But maybe I've found my sport."

22. Which words from the story show that Ricardo wasn't confident about himself?
A. "So why aren't I good at something?"
B. "Hey, you're pretty good," Ricardo said.
C. "That was great!" the girl said.
D. "You want to try it?"

23. How does the writer show that Juan cares about Ricardo?
A. Juan drove Ricardo to the soccer field.
B. Juan went to practice, but Ricardo got bored.
C. Juan tells Ricardo that he will find his sport.
D. Juan was a great soccer player.

24. If this story continued, what role would the girl on the archery range play?
A. She would end up winning an archery contest.
B. She would not be mentioned again.
C. She would probably become friends with Juan and Ricardo.
D. She would give up archery and learn to play soccer.

The sign on the door read, "X-Ray." Jesse hopped into a small room with only a bed and some big equipment. He jumped up onto the bed with one foot. Slowly he eased his right leg up. As he sat in the quiet room, he began to feel his ankle pulse. What could he do to take his mind off the pain? Jesse scanned the room and noticed a poster just across from the bed. The pictures explained all the bones in the foot and leg.

25. Jesse will probably find a way to stop thinking about his ankle by
    A. walking over to a magazine rack.
    B. playing with the big equipment.
    C. reading the poster about bones.
    D. lying down on the bed to sleep.

Sarita waited anxiously outside the trailer. She had looked forward to this trip to Grammy's all summer. When she arrived yesterday, Grammy promised to show her how to catch a fish. As Sarita tried to picture a live fish, Grammy came outside and told her they had to find some bait before they could leave. Bait? They needed worms for bait, and she certainly hadn't seen any worms in this dry country. Grammy told Sarita to follow her to a patch of moist dirt. Grammy had dumped their leftovers there the night before. As Grammy sifted the dirt, the whole patch came alive. Sarita looked closer and saw long, pink, slimy things. Grammy handed her an empty coffee can.

26. How will Sarita probably find bait?
    A. collect worms from the moist dirt
    B. look for bugs on the way to the lake
    C. go to the bait store down the street
    D. use the leftovers from the night before

Ramon watched from the perfume counter as people gathered outside the door. "Jingle Bells" suddenly rang out over the loud speaker as the manager prepared for the store to open. Ramon's heart beat a little faster. He didn't know how he would be able to remember where all the brands of perfume were located in the counter. His manager came over and asked Ramon how he felt. When Ramon confessed he was nervous, the manager said he would do fine. She reminded him that all the shelves were labeled with each perfume's brand name. She also showed him a map of the perfumes on the counter.

27. How will Ramon probably find perfume?
    A. ask his manager when he is unsure
    B. use the map and shelf labels
    C. ask customers to help him
    D. draw a map for himself

Diagnostic Test
Literary Response and Analysis
Narrative Analysis: Author's Technique and Language

Directions for all questions in this test:

Read each passage and answer the questions that follow it. Some items will have no passage. On the answer sheet, fill in the bubble for the answer you think is correct.

Sample questions:

The building was old and seemed shabby. Randy wasn't sure he wanted to go into this museum, but his mother insisted. "You'll be surprised," she told him. Randy still wasn't convinced and tried to talk his mother out of the visit. Mother opened the huge door and held it while Randy walked in. His jaw dropped when he saw what was inside. There were more dinosaur skeletons than he had ever seen in his life.

---

1. What is the lesson in this story?
   A. Old buildings are built well.
   B. Good things come in small packages.
   C. Things aren't always as they seem.
   D. Old habits are hard to break.

2. Which of these is an example of first-person narrative?
   A. Doris put her backpack on her shoulder.
   B. I was too tired to watch the movie.
   C. "This is a steep hill," said Marty.
   D. You should hang the feeder away from the house.

There was once a scientist who believed that, if he studied the stars carefully enough, he could predict the future. The scientist went for long walks at night with his eyes fixed on the heavens. Refusing to take his eyes off the stars, the scientist tripped and fell into a deep, muddy hole. His cries for help attracted the villagers, who rescued him. One of them said, "You seek to read the future in the stars, but you fail to see what is at your feet!"

1. What lesson can be learned from this story?
   A. The wise do not let themselves be tricked twice.
   B. Do not count your chickens before they hatch.
   C. Hurry in the present, and regret it in the future.
   D. Do not let dreams of the future spoil the present.

Favian Mercado thought it would be neat to run for student-body president, so he did. When the votes were counted, and Favian had won the election, he met with the vice principal to go over his new duties. Afterwards, Favian felt overwhelmed. He had no idea he would have to attend school-board meetings, write monthly reports, and organize the annual fundraiser. If he had known being president would be so much work, he might not have run.

2. The moral of this story is
   A. nothing is worth more than freedom.
   B. with greatness comes responsibility.
   C. misfortune is the test of friendship.
   D. common sense is a valuable treasure.

When Wilma Rudolph was four, she got terribly sick and came down with polio. Wilma's doctors said she was crippled and would never walk again. But Wilma was determined to walk. With the support of her family and years of physical therapy, Wilma was not only able to walk but to play on the basketball team. A basketball championship eventually led Wilma to college and a successful career in track. Then, in 1960, the girl whom doctors said would never walk earned three gold medals at the Olympic Games.

3. The theme of this story is
   A. listen to and follow the advice of experts.
   B. it is better to give up than to be stubborn.
   C. you can do whatever you put your mind to.
   D. be satisfied with what you have been given.

Daniel Parsons lives at the intersection of 44th Avenue and Stanton, just four blocks from the hospital. Neighbors call him "Doc" and often stop to visit the retired doctor. Doc was a great doctor because he truly cared about people. When he first retired, he sorely missed the daily interaction with patients. So he moved a big comfortable chair to his front porch, and he sits there when the weather permits. Doc seems cheered by his visits with the people who pass by. Many of them are his former patients.

4. According to the story, being a good doctor means
   A. living near the hospital.
   B. having a caring personality.
   C. getting plenty of fresh air.
   D. enjoying many houseguests.

Dolores was a close friend of my mother, but, for the longest time, we thought she came to our house just to be with us kids. For us, a visit from Dolores meant hours of undivided attention. She read stories and worked on puzzles with us. She got us started collecting rocks and even taught us how to count in Spanish. One day, we asked Dolores if she had any children of her own. She said she did, but they were all grown up. "It's a good thing I have you," she said smiling.

5. What does Dolores do to indicate she is there to visit the kids?
   A. She spends all her time playing with them.
   B. She only visits when their mother is away.
   C. She has nothing else to do with her time.
   D. She is not very friendly toward their mother.

Jamal sat waiting for the ski lift to take him up the slope. It was early yet, and the slopes had just opened. The snow was a sea of perfect, fluffy, whiteness that lay undisturbed and peaceful. It is a brand new day, Jamal thought, looking out over the fresh snow. He took a deep breath and felt the crisp morning air fill his lungs. He felt better already, and he hadn't even gotten off the lift.

6. How does the story's setting seem to affect Jamal?
   A. It makes him feel proud.
   B. It seems to concern him.
   C. It seems to inspire him.
   D. It makes him feel lonely.

Long ago, a dragon flew to Wawel Hill in the country now known as Poland. This dragon was especially horrible. He made his new home in a roomy cave beneath the hill. The dragon ate grazing cattle and attacked the small town nearby. Wawel Hill, once a lovely spot, had become a place filled with fear.

The king was greatly troubled by this dragon. He sent out a call to all the greatest knights in the land to defeat this terrible monster. One by one, the knights tried to overcome the dragon. All of them failed.

One day, a handsome young man appeared at the castle. He wore the clothes of a peasant, but his voice was strong and brave. "I am Krak, the shoemaker," the young man said. "I will defeat the dragon."

The king had heard things like this before. He nodded his head sadly. The princess looked at the man with pity. She was sure he would not succeed.

Krak stuffed a cow's hide with sulfur, a fiery poison. He placed what looked to be a tasty meal at the entrance to the dragon's cave. The greedy dragon swallowed the whole thing in one mouthful. At once, the dragon's throat burned, and it ran to the nearby river. The dragon gulped so much water that it burst with a great bang. The land was free of the dragon at last.

The princess admired the brave shoemaker. They were married, and after the king's death, Krak became the new king of the land. It is said that the town he rescued from the dragon changed its name to honor the shoemaker. It is now known as Krakow.

7. Which idea from this story is often found in other tales?
   A. A river is near a city.
   B. Wawel Hill was once a lovely spot.
   C. A poor man wins a great victory.
   D. A dragon drinks a lot of water.

8. Which of these other tales would probably be like the story of Krak and the dragon?
   A. A girl finds a secret world inside a mirror.
   B. A mountain is named after a general who defeats the enemy.
   C. An explorer finds a hidden cave where a great treasure is buried.
   D. A sculptor makes a statue that becomes a real person.

9. What did Krak do that characters in many other stories have done?
   A. failed often before he finally succeeded
   B. stuffed a cow's hide with sulfur, a fiery poison
   C. made shoes before he was a hero
   D. showed that being smart is better than being strong

10. Which of these is an example of *simile*?
   A. The thunder boomed like an angry drum.
   B. Our crab apple trees were in full bloom.
   C. The dog heard the whistle and jumped.
   D. A blanket of dew lay over the fields.

11. Which of these is an example of *metaphor*?
   A. The poppies opened in the afternoon sun.
   B. The prairie was a sea of rolling green.
   C. The women chattered quickly and noisily.
   D. The small boat was tossed all night long.

12. Which of these is an example of *onomatopoeia*?
   A. The ground was covered with leaves.
   B. We learned a song about a redwood tree.
   C. The houses looked like little boxes.
   D. All we heard was the buzzing of bees.

13. Which of these is an example of *hyperbole*?
   A. The classroom was quiet while they worked.
   B. The strawberries were ready to be picked.
   C. The basketball player had legs like skyscrapers.
   D. The president's speech inspired the crowd.

14. Which of these is an example of *personification*?
   A. My mother's father was a doctor in New York.
   B. The lonely house stood on a hill by itself.
   C. Tomatoes are best when you grow them yourself.
   D. The bicyclist got hurt before the race began.

15. Why would an author use simile?
   A. to make the reader laugh at something that normally isn't funny
   B. to give the reader a better idea of what something sounds like
   C. to help the reader understand one thing by comparing it with another
   D. to show how people long ago are like people today

16. What would be the purpose of using onomatopoeia to describe a mountain stream?
   A. so the reader would understand what it looked like
   B. so the reader would understand what it sounded like
   C. so the reader would understand where it was
   D. so the reader would understand where it was flowing to

17. The stories of Paul Bunyan make great use of hyperbole. What is the effect of using hyperbole in these stories?
   A. It shows that Paul Bunyan really liked Babe, the blue ox.
   B. It lets the reader see that Paul Bunyan is much like other people.
   C. It compares Paul Bunyan to other people in legends.
   D. It makes Paul Bunyan seem more powerful than a regular person.

> My sister knows no strangers. Even as a young girl, Laura would talk to anyone, anywhere, and at anytime.

18. The author is trying to tell you that Laura
  A. is interesting.
  B. is talkative.
  C. is funny.
  D. is intelligent.

> You can always tell when school is closed for spring vacation. Flocks of teenagers fill the mall from morning until night.

19. According to the author, what happens during spring break?
  A. Most teenagers fly somewhere for vacation.
  B. Many teenagers forget what they've learned.
  C. Large numbers of teenagers go shopping.
  D. Very few teenagers hang out and relax.

> The grapefruit hung like yellow bowling balls from the tree's lower branches. Celine picked a few to bring to her grandfather.

20. What is the author trying to tell you about the grapefruit?
  A. They are black.
  B. They have holes.
  C. They are sweet.
  D. They are large.

> Like the teller of stories, the quilt was full of tales. Each scrap of cloth contained a memory. Here was part of the shirt Ben wore his first day of school. Beside it was a scrap from Mother's prom dress.

21. The author's words create the impression that the quilt
  A. was a living thing.
  B. looked strange.
  C. was made by Mother.
  D. seemed to be falling apart.

"We need some volunteers for this scene. Who will read the part of Romeo?" Mr. Jaeger asked the class.

Jeremy raised his hand eagerly. "I will!" he said.

"I want to read, too," I said. "But only if I get the part of Juliet," I told Mr. Jaeger with a smile.

"That's fine, Beverly, but we still need one more person," said Mr. Jaeger. "We need someone to be the nurse."

William raised his hand. "Does the nurse have to be female?" he asked shyly.

"Not in Shakespeare's day, and not in ours," said Mr. Jaeger. "Come on up!"

---

22. Who is telling the story?
   A. Mr. Jaeger
   B. Jeremy
   C. Beverly
   D. William

"Did you read this?" I asked my parents, shoving the travel section of the newspaper toward them.

"No—should we?" Dad asked absentmindedly, munching on his toast.

Mom was more curious. "What is it, Gus, dear?" she asked. "Something for a current-events assignment?"

"Better," I said enthusiastically. "It's an article that tells how to plan a great vacation with your teenager."

"Hmmmmm," said Dad showing more interest. "Let me have a look at that."

---

23. You can tell this story is written in first person because
   A. the story is being told by one of the characters.
   B. there are two or more characters in the story.
   C. you know what each of the characters are thinking.
   D. there is dialogue and conversation in the story.

"Welcome, and thank you for coming," Mr. Escobar was saying as Mitch got out of the pick-up truck and approached the parking lot filled with people. Mr. Escobar was pleased to see such a large group of tree-planting volunteers.

"The holes have already been dug at different locations throughout the neighborhood," Mr. Escobar told everyone.

Mitch was puzzled, so he raised his hand. "How will we know which trees go where?" he asked.

"Good question," said Mr. Escobar. "Each tree has a label showing the address where it is to be planted."

---

24. You can tell that this story is written in third person because
   A. there is dialogue and conversation in the story.
   B. there are at least three people in the story.
   C. the story is being told by one of three characters.
   D. the story tells what the characters are thinking.

The Soccer Game

On the morning of the big game, the butterflies in my stomach seemed huge. I was so nervous I could barely tie my shoelaces—me, Ally Hayes, goalie for the Summerville Slammers! I wanted my first game to be great.

When the game started, all I could think about was defending the goal. I remembered everything my coach, Mr. Quinn, showed us in practice. The game was exciting. I blocked two kicks by the other team and the crowd yelled and clapped for me. Then, at the end of the game, disaster struck. As I ran to block another kick, my foot twisted. They made the goal and won the game. But my foot hurt so bad that I fell in a heap. I tried not to cry, but it was hard. Everyone on the team stood over me as the coach carried me off the field. It was only a sprain, but I was out of the game.

The Soccer Game

I don't much like soccer, but it's important to my little sister Ally. When she made goalie on her team, it was a big deal around the house. The whole family, including me, her big brother, went to see her first game.

I could tell she was nervous by the look on her face. She kept holding her stomach like it hurt. But she was determined to make her first game a good one.

Mom, Dad, and I sat on the metal bleachers and watched the game. Ally was great. She blocked the first two attempts by the opposing team. She was a natural on the field. The whole team played very well. There was only a minute left in the game when something happened to Ally. She fell as she tried to block a kick. The Flames won the game. We all rushed to the field to see what was wrong. Ally had sprained her ankle. She was upset that the Flames had won the game, but we told her that there would be other games.

The Soccer Game

Minnville Flames defeat Summerville Slammers; Goalie Injured
reported by Dan Good, sportswriter

The action at Saturday's soccer match between the undefeated Minnville Flames and the Summerville Slammers didn't disappoint anyone who witnessed it. The Flames, the city's champion Junior Soccer team, has a season record of 4-0. The Slammers record is 3-1, but they have a strong group of players and a good coach, Mr. Jerimiah Quinn.

The Slammers made a good effort to break that winning streak Saturday morning. Fancy footwork by the Slammers' new goalie, Ally Hayes, kept the Flames from scoring two much-needed goals at the beginning of the game. At the end of the game, however, Ally was injured while trying to block the Flames' winning goal. The Slammers' coach, Mr. Quinn, was quoted as saying, "It's just a sprain. She'll be fine for our next game."

25. How did does the mood of the first story change?
  A. from worried to nervous to sad
  B. from excited to nervous to worried
  C. from nervous to worried to excited
  D. from nervous to excited to disappointed

26. Why did the writer of the second story go to the game?
  A. because it was important to Ally
  B. because he liked soccer
  C. because he was worried about Ally
  D. because his parents made him

Continued on page 53.

27. Who probably wrote the third story?
  A. a coach
  B. a sports reporter
  C. a losing player
  D. a winning player

28. Read this line from a poem by Rudyard Kipling. Why do you think he wrote this way?

> You talk o' better food for us, an' schools, an' fires, an' all:

  A. to confuse the reader about the poem
  B. to make it hard for the reader to understand
  C. to show it was a common person speaking
  D. to make the reader feel a sense of danger

29. What feeling is created in this line from a poem by T. S. Eliot?

> Under the brown fog of a winter noon

  A. excited
  B. gloomy
  C. busy
  D. joy

30. Why does the poet repeat the word "break" so often in these lines of poetry?

> Break, break, break,
>   On thy cold gray stones, O Sea!

  A. to show that waves are coming in again and again
  B. to show how much damage waves can do
  C. to show that the sea broke the stones
  D. to show that the gray stones are cold and near the sea

Diagnostic Test
Literary Response and Analysis
Literary Criticism

Directions for all questions in this test:

Read each passage and answer the questions that follow it. Some items will have no passage. On the answer sheet, fill in the bubble for the answer you think is correct.

Sample questions:

No one knew Mr. Appleby very well. He seemed friendly enough, but it was hard to get to know him. He traveled often, and when he was home, strange people were always visiting him. Once, a huge limousine parked in front of his house, and some important-looking people walked into his house. A few minutes later, they walked out again and drove away. It was little things like this that caused people to make up stories about Mr. Appleby.

---

1. How does the author make Mr. Appleby seem mysterious?
   A. by giving just hints about him
   B. by making him seem important
   C. by saying he was friendly
   D. by talking about made-up stories

2. Which of these characters seems least believable?
   A. Matt threw his baseball glove on the floor, took his shoes off, and flopped on the bed.
   B. When Mollie heard the phone ring, she dashed down the stairs to answer it.
   C. Although she was just twelve, Susan had already graduated from college.
   D. Harvey had the biggest music collection in the neighborhood, more than fifty CDs.

The people of the region had lived in fear for years. An invading army had dethroned their queen, a kind and just ruler. In her place, the invaders had raised a false king. He was cruel and unjust, but his army was strong.

Recently, their hopes had risen. A band of rebels had been fighting the cruel king's army and winning. The rebel leader, a fearless woman, was rumored to be the real queen.

1. What do the king and queen in this story represent?
   A. people looking for a new land
   B. two ways to solve a problem
   C. the fight of good against evil
   D. why people should help one another

No one thought much of Allen. He was too much of a dreamer. While the other boys learned a trade, Allen dreamed of becoming a knight. This was impossible, of course, because he was just the son of a farmer.

One day, the villagers woke to a strange sight. Allen was wearing a suit of armor he had made from old pots and pans. He sat on a plow horse he had borrowed from his father. He was armed with nothing more than a woodsman's axe and a butcher's knife. Allen said he was on his way to find the Heart of the Mountain. This stone was said to give the finder the gifts of courage, wisdom, and strength.

2. What symbol can the Heart of the Mountain best be compared to?
   A. a pool of water in the desert that saves a thirsty traveler
   B. a sword that will make the person who carries it a king
   C. a magic mountain that no one can climb
   D. a ghost ship that appears only once in a hundred years

When Randy was accused of stealing some money from the science club, he lost almost all his friends. Even his teachers said they were disappointed. The only person who stuck by him was his best friend, Julia. For almost a week, the other kids in school had said bad things about both of them. Then, on Friday afternoon, two girls found a box with the missing money. It had fallen behind a table in the science room. Everyone felt terrible for how they had treated Randy and Julia.

3. This story is an example of a person who
   A. makes a bad decision.
   B. makes mistakes but isn't caught.
   C. is a hero by accident.
   D. puts loyalty ahead of everything else.

No matter how hard she tried, Jessica couldn't make plants grow. Each summer her mom and dad planted a tomato garden in the backyard. Mom and Dad's tomatoes grew round and ruby red. Jessica's plants were stumpy and shriveled.

This bothered Jessica greatly. "I'm a danger to plants," she thought sadly one morning as she dumped yet another dead tomato plant in the garbage. "I have the blackest thumb in town."

"Did you say you have a black thumb?" a voice said. The backyard gate opened, and a tiny, plump woman appeared. She was wearing a bright green dress and a large green straw hat. "Maybe I can help you."

The lady handed Jessica a small bag filled with black dirt. "Put this on your plants," she said. Then, the stranger winked and disappeared.

Jessica was ready to try anything. The next day she sprinkled the dirt in her garden. She even put some in each of the houseplants. She watered the plants, cut off some brown leaves, and waited. Within weeks, her tomato plants were growing tall and green. All the houseplants grew so fast that they had to be repotted. Jessica and her mom were kept busy repotting the plants and picking baskets full of tomatoes.

One afternoon, Jessica was hauling another basket of tomatoes to the kitchen when the lady in green appeared again. "How's the garden?" she asked.

"What was that stuff?" Jessica cried. "It's great!"

"Nothing," the green lady said with a smile. "It was just dirt with a little compost."

"But the plants grew so well," Jessica stammered.

"You just needed to believe you could do it," the woman said. "When you believed, you took better care of the plants and they started to grow. You never had a black thumb, child, just a can't-do attitude."

With that, the lady in green winked again and disappeared through the gate.

4. How does the writer create a feeling of mystery in this story?
   A. by describing how the plants grew quickly
   B. by telling how Jessica was not good with plants
   C. by talking about how Jessica is ready to try anything
   D. by not explaining who the lady in green is

5. In the beginning of the story, the writer makes you believe that Jessica
   A. wants to keep trying.
   B. seems disappointed in herself.
   C. worries about her parents.
   D. shows that she enjoys eating tomatoes.

6. How does the writer first hint that the black dirt is not magical?
   A. by showing that Jessica is taking better care of her plants
   B. by having the lady in green wink at Jessica at the end of the story
   C. by suggesting that Jessica has a black thumb
   D. by having Jessica say the plants grew so well

Evan and Toby had been best friends for as long as they could remember. Both of the boys had July birthdays and had grown up on the same street. Evan and Toby spent as much time together as possible, especially during the summer months. During the day, they could be found in the pool at Toby's house. After dark, the two were often camped out in a tent in Evan's backyard. This continued into elementary school and junior high. Only the activities changed as the boys became interested in different things.

7. How does the writer make the boys seem real?
   A. by giving them unusual names
   B. by telling what they like to do
   C. by describing where they live
   D. by comparing their differences

Jerry and Aunt Marni were preparing a garden bed. They had marked off an area and were turning the soil when Jerry's shovel hit something hard. Jerry and Aunt Marni kneeled down to take a closer look. Buried about six inches below the surface was an unusual green jar. "Wow," said Jerry as he pulled the treasure up out of the loosened soil. "It's an old juice jar," marveled Aunt Marni. "Let's clean it up and take it to the antique store. They'll tell us what it's worth."

8. Which of these best describes the plot of this story?
   A. It seems like a fairy tale because it has buried treasure and a happy ending.
   B. It seems impossible because a bottle that was buried would have been broken.
   C. It seems make-believe because bottles get recycled not buried in people's yards.
   D. It seems realistic because sometimes things that have been buried are found later.

When Julianne got home from school, she was tired. She did not want to get too comfortable, though. She had homework for every class and needed to get busy right away. Otherwise she wouldn't get it all done. But Julianne's mother had a different idea. "No girl of mine goes to school all day and then has to do homework, no sir." Julianne's jaw dropped as her mother continued. "No more homework for you, my sweet. Here's the phone. Why don't you lie down and call a couple of friends? Your father and I don't think you've been using the phone enough." *Am I dreaming?* Julianne thought, pinching herself.

9. Why is this story not very believable?
   A. Students don't usually have homework.
   B. Mothers don't usually tell their children not to do homework.
   C. Students don't get tired after school.
   D. Mothers don't care how their children spend their time.

A seventh grade girl named Rachel read this story and shared it with her family and friends. Read the story and think about Rachel when you answer the questions.

Quest for the Treasure was Darla's favorite computer game. She played a brave warrior queen character who ruled the land of Pavlovia. The more battles Darla's character won, the more gold and riches her character got.

One day, Darla lost track of time as she played. Her character trapped a large troll and found his stash of gold and gemstones. When Darla finally finished, she noticed that dawn was breaking outside. She had played all night!

Darla walked into the kitchen, her stomach growling. "I'm hungry. What's for breakfast?" she asked Mom, who was standing by the refrigerator.

"Oh brave queen, I have no food worthy of your greatness," Mom said as she left the kitchen.

"Weird," Darla thought as she got a bowl of cereal.

Soon, her little brother came into the kitchen. When he saw Darla, he fell to his knees, trembling.

"What's the matter with you?" Darla said, annoyed.

"Oh, please, fierce warrior, do not slay me!" he mumbled, crawling out of the kitchen backward.

"What's wrong with everybody?" she said aloud. Suddenly her bowl of cereal looked suspiciously like gruel. She put it in the sink and went back to her room.

But something was wrong. Her bed had been replaced by a dirty blanket on the floor. Her computer desk was piled with used armor, pieces of weapons, and glass vials holding colored liquids. Stacks of gold and gems glinted in the morning light. And in the corner stood a huge, green, lumpy, snarling troll.

Darla felt a hand on her shoulder, and jumped. Slowly, she looked around. Her mother was behind her, smiling. Her room was just as it had been. She blinked her eyes a few times to wake herself up. "I think you'll sleep better in bed than with your head on your desk," she heard her mother say.

---

10. Rachel's little brother read this story and said he sometimes feels like Darla's brother. What did he probably mean?
 A. Sometimes he acts like a fierce warrior.
 B. Sometimes he feels like a troll.
 C. Sometimes he likes to play computer games.
 D. Sometimes he is a little afraid of Rachel.

11. Rachel's father said there was a lesson in the story for Rachel. What was the lesson?
 A. that she shouldn't spend so much time on the computer
 B. that she was spending too much outside playing sports

C. that she had too much stuff in her room
D. that she should not get up so early in the morning

12. Rachel's friend, Manuel, liked the story, particularly the setting. Which of these stories would he probably like, too?
 A. A president's daughter goes to a regular school.
 B. A pilot flies her plane around the world by herself.
 C. A boy gets lost in a forest and finds a magic kingdom.
 D. A troll lives under a bridge and chases people.

Diagnostic Test
Vocabulary and Concept Development

General Directions:

This test is made up of 66 questions. Read the directions before each set of questions. Mark all of your answers on the answer sheet. Mark each answer by filling in the bubble for the choice you think is correct. Try these sample questions. Mark your answer on the answer sheet.

Sample Questions:

1. Which of these words means about the same thing as huge?
   A. tiny
   B. hug
   C. animal
   D. large

Directions: Find the word that is missing in this sentence.

2. Even though she did not win the contest, Patti did not _____.
   A. project
   B. deject
   C. object
   D. reject

Directions: Read each sentence. Choose the word that has the opposite meaning of the underlined word. On the answer sheet, fill in the bubble for the answer you think is correct.

1. Sometimes Sara would defy her friends when they told her she should do her homework.
   A. answer
   B. listen to
   C. obey
   D. reject

2. Antonio's father has a portable computer that he brings home from work with him.
   A. stationary
   B. folding
   C. colorful
   D. expensive

3. Marta told Kim that she had a novel solution to their problem.
   A. a complete
   B. a scientific
   C. an ordinary
   D. an easy

Directions: Read each sentence. Choose the word that means the same thing as the underlined word in the sentence. On the answer sheet, fill in the bubble for the answer you think is correct.

4. Victoria thought that it was absurd to have only one week to complete the entire term paper.
   A. intelligent
   B. unreasonable
   C. timely
   D. busy

5. Mario appeared weak and gaunt after his surgery.
   A. healthy
   B. behind
   C. angry
   D. thin

6. After he was tackled, Thomas lay prone on the field trying to find the strength to get up.
   A. trembling
   B. flat
   C. hurt
   D. pinned under

Directions: Read each sentence. Choose the correct meaning of the underlined word. On the answer sheet, fill in the bubble for the answer you think is correct.

7. The trunk of the River Birch looked as if someone had stripped off the bark.
   A. tree covering
   B. dog's sound
   C. small boat

8. Whenever Nathan visited his grandfather, animals would bay in the woods and awaken him at night.
   A. an herb
   B. howl
   C. reddish brown color

9. Because he had no sinker, Joe watched the worm on his hook bob on top of the water.
   A. weight on the end of a line
   B. move up and down
   C. nickname for Robert

Directions: Read each sentence. Find the meaning of the underlined word. On the answer sheet, fill in the bubble for the answer you think is correct.

10. Mary claims to be <u>antiestablishment</u>, but she still decided to run for student council.
A. against stores
B. opposed to education
C. against government
D. opposed to elections

11. The class <u>begrudgingly</u> agreed to give the school half of their treasury to repair the damage.
A. with a grudge
B. agreeing generously
C. with a greeting
D. adding interest

12. Sandy gave a <u>passionate</u> speech that convinced the soccer team to buy new uniforms.
A. without possibility
B. with emotion
C. progressive
D. not impressive

Directions: Read each sentence. Find the meaning of the underlined word. On the answer sheet, fill in the bubble for the answer you think is correct.

13. The police officer said, "One of the best ways to protect your home against crime is to <u>illuminate</u> the area around it."
A. patrol
B. fence
C. light
D. wire

14. As Robert attempted to replace the faucet, he <u>ruptured</u> a pipe and had to call a plumber to fix both problems.
A. buried
B. replaced
C. discovered
D. broke

15. Rae Ann decided that she wanted a career in <u>aeronautics</u>.
A. involving aircraft
B. involving the sea
C. astronomy
D. mechanical engineering

Directions: Read each sentence. Find the meaning of the underlined word. On the answer sheet, fill in the bubble for the answer you think is correct.

16. Following Mrs. Ladd's <u>admonition</u>, we all sat down quietly.
A. request to parents
B. mild warning
C. leadership
D. loud scolding

17. Sonia's baby brother was coughing so much his mother took him to the <u>pediatrician</u>.
A. children's medical specialist
B. doctor who treats lung problems
C. a pharmacist who helps children
D. an x-ray technician

18. No sooner had Nancy and Raymond met than there was <u>antipathy</u> between them.
A. admiration
B. competition
C. attraction
D. dislike

Directions: Read each sentence. Find the meaning of the underlined word. On the answer sheet, fill in the bubble for the answer you think is correct.

19. Shirley could feel her enthusiasm <u>ebb</u> with each passing moment.
  A. lessen
  B. expand
  C. replace itself
  D. rise

20. Steve's method of <u>heaving</u> boxes of eggs around the store made me very nervous.
  A. moving quickly
  B. sliding smoothly
  C. stacking very high
  D. lifting and throwing

21. No sooner was Mary out of <u>earshot</u> than Diane started telling funny stories.
  A. sight
  B. firing range
  C. hearing distance
  D. personal space

Directions: Read the blended word in all capital letters. Choose the words that went together to form that blended word. On the answer sheet, fill in the bubble for the answer you think is correct.

22. BRUNCH
  A. brush + inch
  B. break + crunch
  C. bread + bunch
  D. breakfast + lunch

23. MOPED
  A. mop + edge
  B. move + pull + down
  C. model + peddler
  D. motor + pedal

24. THERMOMETER
  A. thermal + meter
  B. theory + met + her
  C. the + mom + better
  D. there + moment + term

Directions: Read the words in all capital letters. These words are formed by combining several other words. Find the words that combine to make up the capitalized word. On the answer sheet, fill in the bubble for the answer you think is correct.

25. ASAP
  A. after + speaking + and + praying
  B. away + safe + and + protected
  C. alone + successfully + away + peacefully
  D. as + soon + as + possible

26. CEO
  A. company + employed + owner
  B. cash + expense + organizer
  C. chief + executive + officer
  D. car + expert + operator

27. ATM
  A. account + thrift + manager
  B. additional + tax + merchant
  C. affordable + terminal + money
  D. automatic + teller + machine

Directions: Read the words in each box. These are foreign words frequently used in the United States. Find the English meaning of each word or phrase. On the answer sheet, fill in the bubble for the answer you think is correct.

28. bravo
    A. Watch out!
    B. You are very brave.
    C. a shout of approval
    D. someone who brags a lot

29. bon voyage
    A. It was a rough trip.
    B. I need a vacation.
    C. Have a good journey.
    D. What a large ship!

30. et cetera
    A. and so forth
    B. it is certain
    C. be very careful
    D. everyone

Directions: Read each sentence. Choose the correct meaning of the underlined word. On the answer sheet, fill in the bubble for the answer you think is correct.

31. We were unable to discover the root of the rumors.
    A. part of a plant
    B. to cheer
    C. search about
    D. source

32. Many of us had learned to be cautious in dealing with representatives of the press.
    A. push against
    B. news media
    C. a large machine
    D. move forward

33. Lucy asked Alex to help her plan the graduation exercise.
    A. homework
    B. physical activity
    C. program
    D. skills

Directions: Read each sentence. Find the meaning of the underlined words. On the answer sheet, fill in the bubble for the answer you think is correct.

34. As a member of the student council, Dennis would often lobby other student groups to raise money for support of council projects.
    A. influence legislation
    B. represent
    C. try to persuade
    D. an entrance hall

35. In contrast to her respectful behavior at home, Georgia was surprisingly impudent to her teachers.
    A. polite
    B. intelligent
    C. rude
    D. impressive

36. Although the Smith's house was built in 1890, they have furnished it with contemporary furniture.
    A. antique
    B. upholstered
    C. expensive
    D. modern

Directions: Read each sentence. Find the meaning of the underlined word as it is used in the sentence. On the answer sheet, fill in the bubble for the answer you think is correct.

37. After Alyssa weighed each of the packages, she calculated the <u>mean</u>.
   A. intend
   B. total
   C. average
   D. unkind

38. The outcome of the game went <u>counter</u> to what all of the experts had predicted.
   A. a long restaurant table
   B. better
   C. opposite
   D. someone who calculates

39. Grandma Reed gently brushed Vicki's long <u>jet</u> hair.
   A. black
   B. type of airplane
   C. stream of water
   D. curly

Directions: Choose the word for the blank that best fits the meaning of each sentence. On the answer sheet, fill in the bubble for the answer you think is correct.

40. Dr. Marconi has conducted that operation so often that he is considered _____.
   A. skilled
   B. able
   C. adept
   D. expert

41. The memories of the deadly accident continued to _____ Rena both day and night.
   A. worry
   B. trouble
   C. torment
   D. bother

42. When Debby realized she was so late, she _____ to the train station.
   A. walked
   B. drifted
   C. rushed
   D. went

Directions: Read each sentence. Find the meaning of the underlined words. On the answer sheet, fill in the bubble for the answer you think is correct.

43. No one was sure why Danny was <u>down in the dumps</u>.
   A. hunting
   B. sad
   C. away
   D. thinking

44. Jean's night was going so badly that every joke she told <u>fell flat</u>.
   A. made people laugh
   B. depressed her friends
   C. was not funny
   D. was unusual

45. When the class started arguing loudly, Mr. Jefferson said, "<u>Cut it out</u>, right now!"
   A. stop
   B. debate
   C. take turns
   D. be more respectful

Directions: Read each sentence. Find the sentence that contains an <u>idiom</u>. On the answer sheet, fill in the bubble for the answer you think is correct.

46. A. All the students seemed to know about the surprise celebration that was planned.
  B. Tammy let the cat out of the bag about Donna's surprise party.
  C. Summer is a good time for parties, because they can be outside.
  D. Some people like to have parties in popular restaurants.

47. A. Every person in school says that Tom is a lot of fun.
  B. Susan seems to laugh all day long.
  C. Joan smiled to cover up her mistake.
  D. Eric is off his rocker.

48. A. A new school was opening less than a mile away from the old one.
  B. The students had been asked to move their heavy desks out into the hall.
  C. Bob yelled, "Could you lend me a hand with moving this desk, please!"
  D. The principal said wearily, "Maybe we should have waited to move until summer."

Directions: Read each sentence. Find the sentence that uses an <u>analogy</u>. On the answer sheet, fill in the bubble for the answer you think is correct.

49. A. On the weekend, George and Mary love to go to movies at the mall.
  B. The crowd left the movie theater like a flock of geese headed south in autumn.
  C. The Royal Cinema has lovely red velvet seats that recline and rock.
  D. On Wednesdays the popcorn is flavored with garlic and hot pepper.

50. A. Words often come out of Tanya's mouth like water pouring from an open faucet.
  B. Ingrid and Tamara wonder if she ever thinks before she speaks.
  C. Public speaking ability should be required for a person who wants to be mayor.
  D. Try to be very quiet in the reference section of the media center.

51. A. On Thursdays the entire school seems to be preparing for tests.
  B. The cafeteria at school serves lunches that it calls "brain food."
  C. Many times, the students are very quiet and somewhat unfriendly.
  D. That day, Fred's friendly smile was like an oasis in the desert.

Directions: Read each sentence. Find the sentence that contains a <u>metaphor</u>. On the answer sheet, fill in the bubble for the answer you think is correct.

52. A. Many red geraniums were in the window box.
  B. Several girls gathered in a group in front of school.
  C. The waves left a bubbly necklace on the soft sand.
  D. Always remember the Alamo.

53. A. A patchwork quilt of farms is tucked against the Rocky Mountains.
  B. Uncle Sam is a symbol of the United States.
  C. Wait until first thing tomorrow to open the gifts.
  D. Paul sent Sue several long-stemmed red roses wrapped in tissue paper.

54. A. Remember me until tomorrow.
  B. The old barns had clever advertisements painted on them.
  C. In the distance, tall, skinny buildings scratched the sky.
  D. In the warm morning, dew still glistened in the grass.

Directions: Read each sentence. Find the sentence that contains a simile. On the answer sheet, fill in the bubble for the answer you think is correct.

55. A. Unlike Marie's laughing, sparkling eyes, Nguyen's were like spoons of melted chocolate.
   B. Jamal and Joe were brotherly twins. You never found one without the other.
   C. The ice cream sundae was sweet. The whipped cream made it a treat.
   D. Our tiny dog likes to patrol the garden, protecting us from dangerous creatures he finds in the bushes.

56. A. A talented athlete is said to be poetry in motion.
   B. Sometimes colorful jellyfish make swimming in the ocean a stinging experience.
   C. Dancing couples swirled and twirled around the gym.
   D. Mario ran around the track as fast as a dog just escaping its leash.

57. A. The stars blinked from the dark sky.
   B. The winter weather was wet, windy, and wild.
   C. The fog was thick and gray like a fuzzy wool blanket.
   D. Spring arrived with the first golden daffodil in April.

Directions: Read each sentence. Find the meaning of the underlined words. On the answer sheet, fill in the bubble for the answer you think is correct.

58. The seventh graders' staccato voices beat through the door.
   A. were muffled
   B. sounded musically
   C. went crashing open
   D. were difficult to ignore

59. Light and shadows played among the faces in the bleachers.
   A. some people were in the sun, some in shade
   B. spotlights glared on everyone
   C. rain began to make people scurry
   D. the people's emotions were mixed

60. All hands on deck!
   A. a card player's demand
   B. a request for help
   C. an order given to a ship's sailors
   D. a command to people to show their palms

Directions: Find the meaning of the underlined word or words. On the answer sheet, fill in the bubble for the answer you think is correct.

61. Ms. Mill's rules for the class were set in stone.
   A. not subject to change
   B. based on a long history
   C. unfair and tough
   D. written on the board

62. Sheila's interest in the election campaign was beginning to flag.
   A. become more showy
   B. be patriotic
   C. intensify
   D. decline

63. Andrea noticed that the sailboat began to list slightly.
   A. lean to the side
   B. rock
   C. make a noise
   D. a series in order

Directions: Look at this section of a thesaurus. Use this information to answer the questions below. On the answer sheet, fill in the bubble for the answer you think is correct.

64. Choose another word that could replace the underlined word in the sentence below.

Carrie's generous offer was met with _____.
A. proposal
B. grudge
C. disapprobation
D. uncomplying

65. Which of these is another meaning of the adjective form *refuse*?
A. refusal
B. on no account
C. disengaged
D. recusant

66. Which word or phrase best fits in the blank in this sentence?

Sally liked the painting so much that she decided to _____ $200 for it.
A. proffer
B. invitation
C. for sale
D. dissent

763. OFFER.—*N.* offer, proffer, tender, bid, overture, proposal, proposition; motion, invitation, offering.

V. offer, proffer, present, tender; bid; propose, move, make a motion, start, invite, place at one's disposal; make possible, put forward, press, urge upon, hold out.

volunteer, come forward, be a candidate, offer (or present) oneself, stand for, bid for; seek; be at one's service.

Adj. in the market, for sale, to let, disengaged, on hire; at one's disposal.

764. REFUSAL.—*N.* refusal, rejection, denial, declension, flat (or point-blank) refusal; repulse, rebuff; discountenance, disapprobation.

negation, abnegation, protest, renunciation, disclaimer; dissent, etc., 489; revocation, annulment.

V. refuse, reject, deny, decline, turn down [*slang*], dissent, etc., 489; negative, withhold one's assent; grudge, begrudge; stand aloof; be deaf to, turn one's back upon, discountenance, forewear, set aside.

resist, repel, repulse, rebuff, deny oneself, discard, repudiate, rescind, disclaim, protest.

Adj. uncomplying, deaf to, noncompliant, unconsenting; recusant; dissentient.

Adv. on no account, not for the world, not on your life! [*colloq.*].

Diagnostic Test
Oral Reading Fluency

General Directions

Oral reading fluency is one indicator of a student's reading comprehension. The results of this test should be combined with other formal and informal indicators of a student's comprehension to form an overall assessment of current achievement. See page I-1 for more information.

Three components of fluency are assessed in this test. First, an estimate of the student's reading *rate* is determined. For this measure, it is important to time the reading in seconds. The timing should be inconspicuous; otherwise, students may attempt to read the story too quickly and will make increased numbers of errors. Second, you should record the number of errors made during reading. This will be used to estimate the student's reading *accuracy*. Finally, you will make an overall assessment of the student's *fluency* using the rubric below (or others developed locally).

Time: Record the number of seconds the student takes to read the selection. Begin timing when the student reads the first word of the selection. Record this number on the Score Summary on the Student Record Form.

Errors: Record the number of words the student is unable to read or reads incorrectly. Use the reprinted passage on the Student Record Form to mark these errors as you follow along while the student reads. An error is a misread word, a word left out of the selection, or an extra word inserted in the reading that is not in the selection. Do not count a self-correction as an error. Count all errors, whether or not they change the meaning. It is acceptable to assist students with specific words as they read; however, these should be counted as errors. Do not count minor mispronunciations as errors. Record the number of errors on the Score Summary on the Student Record Form.

Holistic Fluency Rating: Use the rubric below to make an overall assessment of the student's fluency. Make this rating immediately after the student completes the reading.

Fluent: The student reads in phrases, generally long meaningful phrases; some errors are likely, but they do not significantly detract from the overall flow of the reading or the selection's meaning; intonation and expression are generally appropriate.

Somewhat Fluent: The student generally reads in short phrases and/or word groupings of limited length (some word-by-word reading may be shown); some word groupings are not consistent with the overall meaning or flow of the passage; at least several errors are made, but most words are read correctly; expression and intonation are limited and often inconsistent with the selection.

Limited Fluency: The student generally reads word by word; limited word groupings are made and most of these are inconsistent with the selection's meaning or flow; multiple errors are made; expression is weak or nonexistent.

Specific Directions

SAY: **Look at this short story. Read it out loud to me. Read it the way you would read it to a friend. If you come to a word you don't know, try your best. Keep reading until you reach the end.**

Follow the reading with the copy on the Student Record Form, and keep track of errors. Also record the number of seconds the student takes. If students stop reading or stumble with a word, encourage them to go on. Help them with an individual word only after waiting several seconds for them to continue.

Oral Fluency Tests — Student Record Form

Student Passage: Mark student errors

Samantha wrote in her diary every day. She found it very comforting, almost like talking to a friend. She would record the day's events, whether they were routine or special. Some days she wrote just a few sentences. Other days she went on for pages.

If she was worried about something or upset, writing about it helped her sort things out and made her feel better. If something exciting was happening in her life, writing about it was like sharing the experience with a friend. One day, when Samantha was older, she looked forward to opening up her diary and reliving those special days from her childhood.

Score Summary

Number of Words in the Selection	**108**
(minus) Number of Errors	– _____
Number of Correct Words	= _____
(divide by) Time (in seconds)	÷ _____
Correct Words per Second	= _____
(multiply by)	× **60**
Oral Reading Rate (Correct Words per Minute)	= _____
Oral Reading Accuracy	= _____

(# Correct Words / # Words in the Selection)

Holistic Fluency Rating: **Fluent**   _____

Somewhat Fluent _____

Limited Fluency _____

Oral Fluency Tests — Student Passage

Samantha wrote in her diary every day. She found it very comforting, almost like talking to a friend. She would record the day's events, whether they were routine or special. Some days she wrote just a few sentences. Other days she went on for pages.

If she was worried about something or upset, writing about it helped her sort things out and made her feel better. If something exciting was happening in her life, writing about it was like sharing the experience with a friend. One day, when Samantha was older, she looked forward to opening up her diary and reliving those special days from her childhood.

Diagnostic Test
Word Recognition
The San Diego Quick Assessment of Reading Ability

General Directions:

This test is given orally to measure the recognition of words out of context. The test consists of 13 graded word lists from preprimer to eleventh grade. The words within each list are of about equal difficulty. Begin with a list two or three sets below the student's grade level and continue until the student makes three or more errors in a list.

Present the Student Material word list to the student. Use pieces of paper to cover word lists not being read. Mark errors on the Record Form by crossing out each missed word. Mispronunciations can be written down next to the word.

Direct the student to read the first word, and then say, "Next." Direct the student to move the paper down and read the next word each time you say, "Next." Encourage the student to read words that he or she does not know so that you can identify the techniques used for word identification. Wait no longer than five seconds before moving on the next word.

Name _____ Date _____

San Diego Quick Assessment—
Student Record Form

Directions: Begin with a list that is at least two or three sets below the student's grade level. Have the student read each word aloud in that list. Continue until the student makes three or more errors in a list.

Reading Levels: One error, independent level; two errors, instructional level; three errors, frustration level. When testing is complete, record the highest grade level in each of these categories in the spaces below.

Independent _____ Instructional _____ Frustration _____

Preprimer	Primer	Grade 1	Grade 2	Grade 3
see _____	you _____	road _____	our _____	city _____
play _____	come _____	live _____	please _____	middle _____
me _____	not _____	thank _____	myself _____	moment _____
at _____	with _____	when _____	town _____	frightened _____
run _____	jump _____	bigger _____	early _____	exclaimed _____
go _____	help _____	how _____	send _____	several _____
and _____	is _____	always _____	wide _____	lonely _____
look _____	work _____	night _____	believe _____	drew _____
can _____	are _____	spring _____	quietly _____	since _____
here _____	this _____	today _____	carefully _____	straight _____

Grade 4	Grade 5	Grade 6	Grade 7
decided _____	scanty _____	bridge _____	amber _____
served _____	business _____	commercial _____	dominion _____
amazed _____	develop _____	abolish _____	sundry _____
silent _____	considered _____	trucker _____	capillary _____
wrecked _____	discussed _____	apparatus _____	impetuous _____
improved _____	behaved _____	elementary _____	blight _____
certainly _____	splendid _____	comment _____	wrest _____
entered _____	acquainted _____	necessity _____	enumerate _____
realized _____	escaped _____	gallery _____	daunted _____
interrupted _____	grim _____	relativity _____	condescend _____

Grade 8	Grade 9	Grade 10	Grade 11
capacious _____	conscientious _____	zany _____	galore _____
limitation _____	isolation _____	jerkin _____	rotunda _____
pretext _____	molecule _____	nausea _____	capitalism _____
intrigue _____	ritual _____	gratuitous _____	prevaricate _____
delusion _____	momentous _____	linear _____	visible _____
immaculate _____	vulnerable _____	inept _____	exonerate _____
ascent _____	kinship _____	legality _____	superannuate _____
acrid _____	conservatism _____	aspen _____	luxuriate _____
binocular _____	jaunty _____	amnesty _____	piebald _____
embankment _____	inventive _____	barometer _____	crunch _____

San Diego Quick Assessment—Student Material

see	you	road	our	city
play	come	live	please	middle
me	not	thank	myself	moment
at	with	when	town	frightened
run	jump	bigger	early	exclaimed
go	help	how	send	several
and	is	always	wide	lonely
look	work	night	believe	drew
can	are	spring	quietly	since
here	this	today	carefully	straight

decided	scanty	bridge	amber
served	business	commercial	dominion
amazed	develop	abolish	sundry
silent	considered	trucker	capillary
wrecked	discussed	apparatus	impetuous
improved	behaved	elementary	blight
certainly	splendid	comment	wrest
entered	acquainted	necessity	enumerate
realized	escaped	gallery	daunted
interrupted	grim	relativity	condescend

capacious	conscientious	zany	galore
limitation	isolation	jerkin	rotunda
pretext	molecule	nausea	capitalism
intrigue	ritual	gratuitous	prevaricate
delusion	momentous	linear	visible
immaculate	vulnerable	inept	exonerate
ascent	kinship	legality	superannuate
acrid	conservatism	aspen	luxuriate
binocular	jaunty	amnesty	piebald
embankment	inventive	barometer	crunch

Diagnostic Test
Phonic Elements

Sample Questions:

Directions: Read the boxed word. Look at the underlined part of the word. Find the word that has the same sound or sounds as the underlined part. On the answer sheet, fill in the bubble for the answer you think is correct.

1. | cheese |
   A. shadow   **C.** thunder
   B. chicken   **D.** ache

Directions: Read the sentence. Choose the word that correctly fits in the blank. On the answer sheet, fill in the bubble for the answer you think is correct.

2. The walls in the room were _____ blue.
   A. painting   **C.** paints
   B. painter   **D.** painted

Directions: Read each boxed word. Look at the underlined part of the word. Find the word that has the same sound or sounds as the underlined part. On the answer sheet, fill in the bubble for the answer you think is correct.

1. | bl̲ame |
   A. lady
   B. bark
   C. brag
   D. able

2. | cr̲ash |
   A. rack
   B. chance
   C. crop
   D. cent

3. | sm̲ell |
   A. smuggle
   B. scramble
   C. seem
   D. mistake

4. | young̲ |
   A. groan
   B. kingdom
   C. smog
   D. nags

5. | camper̲ |
   A. came
   B. map
   C. pamphlet
   D. stump

6. | hal̲f |
   A. leaf
   B. shelf
   C. left
   D. laugh

7. | sh̲ell |
   A. school
   B. worship
   C. skeleton
   D. perhaps

8. | wr̲inkle |
   A. unwrap
   B. walk
   C. wand
   D. warn

9. | ph̲oto |
   A. perhaps
   B. ships
   C. brief
   D. upon

10. | ra̲cket |
    A. brace
    B. process
    C. stretched
    D. second

11. | autho̲r |
    A. witch
    B. tight
    C. bathtub
    D. there

12. purch̲ase
  A. chemist
  B. paragraph
  C. stuck
  D. touch

13. plain̲
  A. against
  B. aisle
  C. today
  D. animal

14. au̲to
  A. height
  B. flaw
  C. alive
  D. potato

15. grou̲p
  A. look
  B. ground
  C. house
  D. room

16. cha̲rm
  A. cheer
  B. smart
  C. air
  D. hearing

17. ski̲rt
  A. heard
  B. wire
  C. siren
  D. stripe

18. retu̲rn
  A. youth
  B. retire
  C. battery
  D. prune

19. unit̲ed
  A. batted
  B. guaranteed
  C. stadium
  D. untied

20. quote̲
  A. got
  B. route
  C. goat
  D. shooter

21. railr̲oad
  A. tread
  B. brood
  C. parade
  D. erode

22. arou̲nd
  A. awesome
  B. vowel
  C. bought
  D. yellow

23. gow̲n
  A. owner
  B. outside
  C. slowly
  D. borrow

24. toi̲l
  A. foolish
  B. juice
  C. employ
  D. oblige

25. frigh̲t
  A. weight
  B. straight
  C. slightly
  D. eighty

26. enou̲gh
  A. though
  B. stuff
  C. bough
  D. ought

27. repla̲ce
  A. coaches
  B. peace
  C. spice
  D. baseball

Directions: Read each sentence. Choose the word that correctly fits in the blank. On the answer sheet, fill in the bubble for the answer you think is correct.

28. What is the name of your reading _____?
   A. teaching
   B. teach
   C. teaches
   D. teacher

29. The mistaken manager was forced to _____ to her staff.
   A. apologize
   B. apologizes
   C. apology
   D. apologies

30. We spent the week at the nicest two _____ in the area.
   A. beaches
   B. beaching
   C. beach
   D. beached

Directions: Read each boxed word. Choose the correct way to divide the word into syllables. On the answer sheet, fill in the bubble for the answer you think is correct.

31. | birthday |
   A. bir th day
   B. birth day
   C. bir thday
   D. b irth day

32. | positive |
   A. pos i tive
   B. po si tive
   C. pos it ive
   D. p os it ive

33. | graduate |
   A. grad u ate
   B. grad u at e
   C. gra du ate
   D. gr ad u ate

Diagnostic Test
Phonemic Awareness
CORE Phoneme Segmentation Test

General Directions:

You will need eight colored blocks to administer this test. Proceed to the test items only after the student demonstrates understanding of the practice item tasks. When administering the test items, give only general positive feedback. Praise the student for even close approximations to a correct response. Record the student's exact response on the blank line. Then after administering the test, go back and circle whether the response was correct or incorrect. Ask for the "sound" if the student says the letter name. If the student cannot segment the entire word correctly, ask just for the first and last sound. Discontinue testing if the student misses five items in a row.

Directions for Practice Item 1: Lay out on the table eight blocks of assorted colors. Make sure to lay out the blocks in a horizontal line, from left to right. The color of the blocks is not important. However, to demonstrate, use a different colored block for each of the different sounds in the word. After the student completes an item, put the blocks back in the pile.

TEACHER: We are going to use these blocks to show the sounds in a word. Let's say I wanted to show you *sit*. That word has three sounds /s/ /i/ /t/. (Put out one block for each of the sounds as you say them slowly in order.) Can you point to the /s/? Which one is the /t/? Which is the sound in this block (the middle /i/)?
STUDENT: /i/
TEACHER: Now, tell me the three sounds.
STUDENT: /s/ /i/ /t/
TEACHER: Very good! You got that the first time!

If the student gives the names of letters rather than their sounds, say:
TEACHER: Yes, that is how it is spelled. Now can you tell me the sounds the letters make?

Directions for Practice Item 2
TEACHER: If you wanted to show *shop*, how many sounds it that? Use the blocks to show me.

If the student cannot do the segmentation independently, demonstrate the complete segmentation.
TEACHER: The word *shop* has three sounds (lay down a block for each of the sounds as you say them, in left-to-right progression): /sh/ /o/ /p/.

To check the student's understanding, ask
TEACHER: What are the three sounds?
STUDENT: /sh/ /o/ /p/
TEACHER: Which one is /sh/? Which one is /p/? What is the sound of the block in the middle? {/o/}

If the student puts down four blocks, he or she is probably trying to spell the word. Remind the student to attend to sounds rather than letters. Once the student can at least point to the block that represents the correct sound, proceed to the test items.

Name _____ Date _____

CORE Phoneme Segmentation Test— Student Record Form

Directions: Have students use different-colored blocks to show the number of phonemes in each of the practice items. Then, administer the test. Mark "+" to indicate a correct response; mark "–" to indicate an incorrect response. Record students' exact responses in the blank lines.

Practice items:
    sit (s-i-t)
    shop (sh-o-p)

1. thumb (th-u-m)   (+) (–) _____

2. skate (s-k-a-t)   (+) (–) _____

3. shriek (sh-r-e-k)   (+) (–) _____

4. large (l-ar-j)   (+) (–) _____

5. drop (d-r-o-p)   (+) (–) _____

6. flew (f-l-oo)   (+) (–) _____

7. chalk (ch-au-k)   (+) (–) _____

8. germ (j-er-m)   (+) (–) _____

9. spread (s-p-r-e-d)   (+) (–) _____

10. train (tr-a-n)   (+) (–) _____

11. stork (s-t-or-k)   (+) (–) _____

12. bolt (b-o-l-t)   (+) (–) _____

13. glare (g-l-air)   (+) (–) _____

14. crowd (k-r-ou-d)   (+) (–) _____

15. point (p-oi-n-t)   (+) (–) _____

Items Correct _____

Additional Oral Reading Fluency Tests

General Directions

Oral reading fluency assessment should be ongoing. It is recommended that tests be given four times a year. Use the two tests here between administration of the Diagnostic Test and the Mastery Test for Oral Reading Fluency. See page I-1 for more information.

Three components of fluency are assessed in this test. First, an estimate of the student's reading *rate* is determined. For this measure, it is important to time the reading in seconds. The timing should be inconspicuous; otherwise, students may attempt to read the story too quickly and will make increased numbers of errors. Second, you should record the number of errors made during reading. This will be used to estimate the student's reading *accuracy*. Finally, you will make an overall assessment of the student's *fluency* using the rubric below (or others developed locally).

Time: Record the number of seconds the students takes to read the selection. Begin timing when the student reads the first word of the selection. Record this number on the Score Summary on the Student Record Form.

Errors: Record the number of words the student is unable to read or reads incorrectly. Use the reprinted passage on the Student Record Form to mark these errors as you follow along while the student reads. An error is a misread word, a word left out of the selection, or an extra word inserted in the reading that is not in the selection. Do not count a self-correction as an error. Count all errors, whether or not they change the meaning. It is acceptable to assist students with specific words as they read; however, these should be counted as errors. Do not count minor mispronunciations as errors. Record the number of errors on the Score Summary on the Student Record Form.

Holistic Fluency Rating: Use the rubric below to make an overall assessment of the student's fluency. Make this rating immediately after the student completes the reading.

Fluent: The student reads in phrases, generally long meaningful phrases; some errors are likely, but they do not significantly detract from the overall flow of the reading or the selection's meaning; intonation and expression are generally appropriate.

Somewhat Fluent: The student generally reads in short phrases and/or word groupings of limited length (some word-by-word reading may be shown); some word groupings are not consistent with the overall meaning or flow of the passage; at least several errors are made, but most words are read correctly; expression and intonation are limited and often inconsistent with the selection.

Limited Fluency: The student generally reads word by word; limited word groupings are made and most of these are inconsistent with the selection's meaning or flow; multiple errors are made; expression is weak or nonexistent.

Specific Directions

SAY: **Look at this short story. Read it out loud to me. Read it the way you would read it to a friend. If you come to a word you don't know, try your best. Keep reading until you reach the end.**

Follow the reading with the copy on the Student Record Form, and keep track of errors. Also record the number of seconds the student takes. If students stop reading or stumble with a word, encourage them to go on. Help them with an individual word only after waiting several seconds for them to continue.

Oral Fluency Tests— Student Record Form

Student Passage A: Mark student errors

There are many beautiful national parks in the United States. They are a great place to go on vacation, because you can enjoy the natural beauty of mountains and lakes and the great outdoors. You can go camping, boating, and hiking and even see wildlife.

The government protects national parks so that nothing can destroy their natural beauty. They are off-limits to things like hunting, farming, and retail stores. You would never find a shopping mall in a national park!

National parks are a great place to go to escape the noise, pollution, and crowds of many cities.

Score Summary

Number of Words in the Selection   __**98**__

    (minus) Number of Errors   − _____

Number of Correct Words   = _____

    (divide by) Time (in seconds)   ÷ _____

Correct Words per Second   = _____

    (multiply by)   × **60**

Oral Reading Rate   = _____
(Correct Words per Minute)

Oral Reading Accuracy   = _____
(# Correct Words / # Words in the Selection)

Holistic Fluency Rating: **Fluent**   _____

                                           Somewhat Fluent   _____

                                         Limited Fluency   _____

Oral Fluency Tests—
Student Passage A

There are many beautiful national parks in the United States. They are a great place to go on vacation, because you can enjoy the natural beauty of mountains and lakes and the great outdoors. You can go camping, boating, and hiking and even see wildlife.

The government protects national parks so that nothing can destroy their natural beauty. They are off-limits to things like hunting, farming, and retail stores. You would never find a shopping mall in a national park!

National parks are a great place to go to escape the noise, pollution, and crowds of many cities.

Oral Fluency Tests— Student Record Form

Student Passage B: Mark student errors

In the United States, the bald eagle is no longer considered an endangered species. Back in 1963, there were only several hundred eagles. Today, there are over five thousand.

Since they are no longer threatened by hunters, eagles have become more comfortable living closer to people. All they need is clean water, a healthy food supply, and tall trees where they can build nests.

Recently, bald eagles have been found nesting in people's backyards in Florida. Last year, a pair nested in the nation's capital for the first time in half a century and gave birth to an eaglet. The bald eagle has certainly made a comeback!

Score Summary

Number of Words in the Selection	**117**
(minus) Number of Errors	– _____
Number of Correct Words	= _____
(divide by) Time (in seconds)	÷ _____
Correct Words per Second	= _____
(multiply by)	× **60**
Oral Reading Rate Correct Words per Minute)	= _____

Oral Reading Accuracy   = _____
(# Correct Words / # Words in the Selection)

Holistic Fluency Rating: **Fluent**   _____

Somewhat Fluent _____

Limited Fluency _____

Oral Fluency Tests—
Student Passage B

In the United States, the bald eagle is no longer considered an endangered species. Back in 1963, there were only several hundred eagles. Today, there are over five thousand.

Since they are no longer threatened by hunters, eagles have become more comfortable living closer to people. All they need is clean water, a healthy food supply, and tall trees where they can build nests.

Recently, bald eagles have been found nesting in people's backyards in Florida. Last year, a pair nested in the nation's capital for the first time in half a century and gave birth to an eaglet. The bald eagle has certainly made a comeback!

Mastery Test
Reading Comprehension:
Using and Analyzing Structural Features

Directions for all questions in this test:

Read each passage and answer the questions that follow it. Some items will have no passage. On the answer sheet, fill in the bubble for the answer you think is correct.

Sample Questions:

> The area around Algo was settled more than a thousand years ago by Native Americans. They were drawn there by the fertile soil and the river that flowed through the area. When the Spanish arrived in the area about 400 years ago, they established a small settlement and trading post in the area. Over the years, ranchers and farmers joined the earlier settlers of the area, and the town grew. Today, the town has a population of about 5,000, and its rich and varied history is a source of pride to everyone who lives there.

1. How is the information in this paragraph organized?
   A. by time order
   B. by cause and effect
   C. by important idea and supporting details
   D. by comparison and contrast

2. Which of these would be found in the front of a book?
   A. the bibliography
   B. the glossary
   C. the table of contents
   D. the index

1. How does an index help you understand the contents of a book?
   A. It explains why the author wrote the book.
   B. It summarizes the information in each chapter.
   C. It defines the meanings of certain words.
   D. It tells you what page information is on.

2. Books and magazine articles often feature bibliographies. A bibliography is found at the end of a work and lists other books and articles. What is the purpose of a bibliography?
   A. It lets you know what other books or articles the author has written.
   B. It tells you what the author used as resources to write the work.
   C. It describes all of the books and articles the author recommends.
   D. It tells you what books or articles are going to be published soon.

3. Which of these would most likely have a graph as part of a news article?
   A. a story describing damage from a wind storm
   B. a letter to the editor explaining someone's opinion about the mayor of a town
   C. an article about the percentage of people who voted for different candidates
   D. an interview with a famous sports star

4. Meena is reading a news story on the Internet about national parks. One of the buttons on the screen says NEXT. If she clicks on this button, what will happen?
   A. She will see the news for the next day.
   B. She will see the next page of the story.
   C. She will have to do another news search.
   D. She will answer the next question.

5. Which of these would probably be on the front page of a newspaper with a big headline?
   A. the section where movie listings are posted
   B. what kind of weather to expect during the week
   C. which department store is having a huge sale
   D. a story about a disaster in another country

6. A newspaper usually lists the sections it contains and the topics of those sections at the bottom of the front page. Why would a newspaper do this?
   A. to help people find what they are looking for
   B. to give people a short summary of the news
   C. to prove that no part of the newspaper is missing
   D. to show where the newspaper got its information

How can you stay busy without going crazy? The Time Keeper will revolutionize the way you plan your day and your life. With an A to Z address book, a weekly and daily calendar, and entries for a daily checklist, you'll never find yourself missing important events again. The leather-bound Time Keeper comes in four stylish colors and also includes a side wallet for conveniently carrying credit cards, cash, checkbooks, change, and more. Keep up with the times. Buy a Time Keeper.

7. Which of these is included in a Time Keeper?
   A. a watch
   B. a calendar
   C. a credit card
   D. a pencil

Requests for time-off must be given to a supervisor at least one week in advance of the date to be taken off. Employees should fill out a time-off request form indicating the days requested off, hours to be missed, and reason for the time-off request (vacation, doctor visit, personal, etc.). A supervisor should respond within one workday of the submission and contact the employee by memo or in person after a decision is made.

8. How early must a person turn in a request for time off?
   A. one workday before time is taken off
   B. as soon as an employee discovers time off is needed
   C. at least one week in advance of the date needed off
   D. the day the employee will be taking time off

A city council meeting will be held at 7:30 in the evening on Tuesday, September 18. Subjects to be discussed are as follows:
1. Main St. Road-Widening Project
2. City Curfew
3. Annual Budget
If any city resident would like to present additional items before the council, please arrive at seven o'clock that evening to sign up for a speaking time.

9. How would a resident be assigned a time to present additional items at the meeting?
   A. arrive thirty minutes before the meeting to sign up
   B. call a week in advance to be placed on the agenda
   C. sign up for an assignment the day before the meeting
   D. come to the council meeting on Tuesday, September 18

Passage 1

Waking up to a fresh cup of coffee has never been so easy. Percolite Plus offers an auto timer feature that allows you to prepare your coffee the night before. Just pour the water, fill the filter with coffee, and set the timer. The next morning, the aroma of fresh coffee will awaken you. Percolite Plus is your answer to waking up happy.

Passage 2

Percolite Plus is covered under a limited warranty for six months. If the Percolite Plus stops working for any reason within six months of the purchase date, the owner will receive a new Percolite Plus or the total amount paid for the product. The owner must mail the proof of purchase, a dated receipt, and the broken product to the manufacturer's address.

Passage 3

1. Fill the coffee pot with the desired amount of water, using the numbers on the pot as a guide.
2. Pour the water into the chamber at the top of the coffeemaker.
3. Place a small filter in the basket at the top of the coffeemaker.
4. Measure the desired amount of ground coffee and place in the filter.
5. Set the timer, if using the auto timer feature.
6. Move switch to ON or AUTO.

10. The purpose of Passage 1 is to
   A. sell a product.
   B. explain a process.
   C. state a fact.
   D. make an agreement.

11. What information can be found in Passage 2?
   A. product description
   B. list of a product's parts
   C. terms of a warranty
   D. operating instructions

12. Passage 3 explains
   A. what to do if the coffeemaker breaks.
   B. why the coffeemaker is a good product.
   C. when the coffeemaker can be fixed.
   D. how to operate the coffeemaker.

Everyone has a place they call home. The places may look different, but they are all places to eat, sleep, and live. Two types of homes are apartments and condominiums. Apartments are like houses that share walls with other houses. They have several floors, like houses stacked on top of one another. People rent apartments, which means they don't have to sell the home when they decide to move. Condominiums sometimes look like apartments, with several stories and shared walls. However, not all condominiums are "stacked" like apartments. People buy condominiums, which means that they are responsible for selling the condominium when they decide to move.

13. How is the information in this passage organized?
   A. causes and effects are identified
   B. things are ordered by time
   C. similarities and differences are identified
   D. an important idea is supported by facts and opinions

C. S. Lewis was a British writer and teacher at some famous schools in England. In the 1940s, Lewis started writing a series of fairy tales for children. The series was called The Chronicles of Narnia. Lewis had always been a fan of fairy tales and legends. He was embarrassed, however, about loving fairy tales when he was young. He tried to keep it a secret. As he grew up, he remembered the magical stories and decided there was nothing wrong with enjoying them. So he tried his hand at writing stories like the ones he loved to read as a child. The stories became well known throughout England and the United States, and they were read by adults and children alike.

14. Which of these caused C. S. Lewis to write fairy tales?
   A. He remembered enjoying magical stories as a child.
   B. He became a teacher at some famous schools in England.
   C. He was embarrassed about reading fairy tales as a child.
   D. He met someone who asked him to write fairy tales.

Owning a pet teaches responsibility. Pets require regular feeding, grooming, and sometimes walking and playing. Some pets live in cages. Their cages must be cleaned, and the cage lining must be replaced. There are certain animals that need special care. Horses wear shoes that must be cared for. Fish must have clean water to swim in. Some fish even have to live in water that stays a certain temperature. When pet owners go on trips, they must plan for the care of their pet while they are gone. A person can learn a lot from owning a pet.

15. Which of these is an important idea that is supported by the details in the passage?
   A. Some pets have cages that must be cleaned.
   B. Horses wear shoes that must be cared for.
   C. People must take their pets with them on trips.
   D. Owning a pet teaches people responsibility.

In the 1600s, King Louis XIV of France had heard reports of a land full of riches. Eager to claim new land, King Louis sent a French explorer named Rene Robert Cavalier La Salle to the rumored haven. La Salle sailed down the Mississippi River and claimed the land where the river drained, now known as Louisiana.

When La Salle returned to France, he asked King Louis to send French settlers to the land. In the summer of 1684, La Salle led a flotilla of four ships with 300 colonists and sailed from France to the New World.

The ships had trouble finding the opening of the Mississippi River, and La Salle landed on the coast of what is now Texas, thinking he was near the Mississippi River. The four ships were separated, but one ship wrecked somewhere on the La Vaca River in Texas. The survivors settled in the wilderness there.

They set up a fort called Fort St. Louis, but the settlement didn't last long. The settlers ran out of food quickly, and some became sick. Not only that, the group didn't get along with one another, and in 1687, part of the group left to travel north toward Canada.

In 1689, the fort was attacked by Native Americans, and the first French settlement in Texas disappeared. La Salle, who left with the group traveling north in 1687, was later killed by one of his own men on the journey.

16. What land did La Salle first discover?
   A. Canada
   B. Texas
   C. France
   D. Louisiana

17. What happened after the settlers set up Fort St. Louis?
   A. La Salle's ship wrecked on the La Vaca River.
   B. La Salle claimed the land now known as Louisiana.
   C. A group of settlers left the fort and traveled north.
   D. King Louis asked La Salle to explore the new land.

18. How is the information in this passage organized?
   A. by comparison, showing how two locations were similar
   B. by time, giving the events in the order they happened
   C. by importance, giving the most important events first
   D. by contrast, showing how two locations were different

Barry and Garry look so much alike that it is difficult for anyone to tell them apart. That isn't surprising, since they are identical twins. The boys grew up in the country, and Garry still lives on a ranch a few miles out of town. Barry moved to the city, however, and no longer wears cowboy hats and boots like his brother. And while Barry likes to jog, Garry prefers riding horses.

19. How is Barry different from Garry?
  A. Barry grew up in the country.
  B. Barry lives on a ranch.
  C. Barry wears cowboy boots.
  D. Barry likes jogging.

Berries come in all shapes and sizes, and some are more alike than others. The blueberry looks and tastes a lot like the huckleberry, though they are slightly different. Both berries are small and round. A ripe blueberry has a dark blue color, and sometimes the color looks almost black. Huckleberries have a dark purple color. Ripe blueberries tend to be sweet, while huckleberries are a little more tart when ripe.

20. Blueberries and huckleberries are both
  A. round.
  B. blue.
  C. tart.
  D. purple.

Cameras that use film have been around for a long time, and families often have at least one in their home. As technology improves, though, digital cameras become more and more popular. Both cameras recreate images. It is often hard to tell the difference between pictures taken by the different cameras. Their differences lie in how they make images. Cameras with film use light to "stamp" images onto film. Digital cameras are like small computers that make the images using pixels, a grid of tiny dots.

21. How are cameras with film like digital cameras?
  A. They use light to "stamp" images onto film.
  B. They make images using tiny dots.
  C. They make pictures by recreating images.
  D. They have been around for a long time.

Cheryl sat waiting for her friend, Tyson, at their favorite ice cream shop. As Cheryl watched for Tyson, she wondered what his surprise would be.

Tyson had just spent six weeks in the hospital to have his left knee replaced. He had rheumatoid arthritis, and he had been in a wheelchair for as long as Cheryl had known him. Tyson would eventually have to have all of his major joints replaced. Although Tyson stayed positive, Cheryl knew the surgeries were difficult for him.

Tyson sounded really excited on the phone, and Cheryl was glad to hear that he wanted to get out. As Cheryl looked out the window one more time, a voice caught her by surprise.

"Hi, stranger!" Cheryl looked around to see Tyson standing with a cane.

"Tyson! You're walking!" Cheryl gave him a hug and began to question him about how he had been able to walk. Tyson settled down in the booth and explained.

"After my surgery, I was really down. I had this big scar on my leg, and I didn't want to do anything but sit in my room. The doctor told me I had to go to the physical therapist and work my new joint."

"While I was there, I met this guy who was twice my age. He'd been in a car wreck, and the doctors told him he'd never walk again. He told me that the only difference between how he walks now and how he walked before the wreck is that it takes him a little longer to get around."

"No one ever told me I could never walk again, and I still have my whole life ahead of me. I decided I want to walk. It just may take me a little longer to get around."

22. Why was Cheryl surprised when she saw Tyson?
  A. Cheryl had not seen Tyson in over a year.
  B. Tyson did not tell Cheryl he was coming.
  C. Tyson was not in a wheelchair anymore.
  D. Tyson did not seem happy when they met.

23. What helped motivate Tyson to walk?
  A. seeing someone else overcome a difficult situation
  B. practicing with a good physical therapist
  C. having surgery to replace his knee joint
  D. being told it would be difficult for him to walk again

24. Why did Tyson have surgery on his knee?
  A. He injured his knee in an accident.
  B. He fell at the ice cream shop.
  C. He hurt his knee playing soccer.
  D. He had rheumatoid arthritis.

Mastery Test
Reading Comprehension:
Evaluating Text

Directions for all questions in this test:

Read each passage and answer the questions that follow it. Some items will have no passage. On the answer sheet, fill in the bubble for the answer you think is correct.

Sample Question:

A typical American supermarket is truly amazing. It is packed with goods of all kinds from every corner of the earth. Chocolates from Switzerland, spices from China, and coffee from Columbia are just a few of the thousands of items available in almost any neighborhood supermarket. Perhaps the most astounding foods are the fresh fruit, vegetables, meat, and fish available any time of the year. Someone from ancient Rome or Victorian England were to visit a supermarket, they would probably believe that it is one of the wonders of the world.

1. What is the main idea of this paragraph?
   A. Food is grown all over the world.
   B. Most supermarkets are in neighborhoods.
   C. Supermarkets are remarkable places.
   D. Ancient Rome and Victorian England are similar.

2. How does the author support the opinion that a supermarket is truly amazing?
   A. by mentioning Ancient Rome and Victorian England
   B. by talking about chocolate, spices, and coffee
   C. by mentioning different countries of the world
   D. by listing things that can be found in a supermarket

1. Felipé wants to write a report about a mountain range called the Andes. He is using an encyclopedia as one of his reference sources. Which of these reading strategies should he use while reading the entry?

   A. He should read the first sentence of each paragraph in the entry.

   B. He should read the entry carefully so he doesn't make a mistake with the facts.

   C. He should skim the entry and look for the key word "Andes."

   D. He should just skim the entry and look for interesting ideas about the Andes.

2. Monique has to give a short report to her class on a current-events newspaper article. After she chooses an article, which of these reading strategies should she use?

   A. She should skim the article for what interests her.

   B. She should read the article until she has memorized it.

   C. She should skim the article then write a few questions.

   D. She should read the article slowly and take some notes.

3. Mr. Thadeus put his students into small groups. The members of each group were given a magazine article on the topic of advertising. During the next five minutes, each student has to read the article then tell the group what it is about. Which of these reading strategies should the students use?

   A. Read slowly and try to remember every detail from the article.

   B. Read only the first and last paragraphs of the article.

   C. Skim the article and try to remember the most important ideas.

   D. Read as quickly as you can so you can read all of the articles.

I groaned when I saw that the first day of summer vacation was sunny and beautiful. My friends were going to spend their days lounging on the beach or playing endless video games. And me? How was I going to spend my summer break? I was volunteering at a camp for kids who were in wheelchairs.

The camp was my mom's idea. She kept insisting that I'd have lots of fun. I don't know what she meant by "fun" because I couldn't think of anything more boring than what I was going to be doing. "If they're in wheelchairs," I muttered to myself, "they won't be able to do anything that is fun."

I arrived at the camp before the kids showed up in time to meet the counselors. I was assigned to help an experienced counselor named Jake, and then I got a big surprise. Jake turned to me and said, "Okay, Kevin, today we're going to be taking the camp horses for a short ride."

"We?" I asked. "Just you and I? I mean, how can kids in wheelchairs ride horses?"

Jake gave me a long, serious look. "The kids go riding every day, Kevin. You've got to forget the idea that these kids can't do anything athletic or enjoyable because they are in wheelchairs. If you can change your attitude, you'll have fun, too."

Since riding horses is my favorite thing in the whole world, right then and there, my attitude changed.

4. This story is mostly about how Kevin discovers that
   A. wheelchairs don't keep kids from having fun
   B. volunteering is a boring way to spend the summer
   C. riding horses is an enjoyable activity
   D. his friends aren't going to camp with him

5. What is the main idea of the second paragraph?
   A. Kevin wants to relax during vacation.
   B. Kevin's mother had fun at camp.
   C. Kevin is sure he won't enjoy camp.
   D. Kevin already knows how to ride.

6. Which of these do you learn in the first paragraph?
   A. Kevin wants to take riding lessons.
   B. Volunteering is Kevin's mom's idea.
   C. Jake is an experienced counselor.
   D. Summer vacation has just started.

Montezuma looked out over the capital. The city appeared golden in the sun's last light, and the kingdom stretched as far as his eyes could see. As a boy, he had heard stories about how his great grandfather's military strength extended these borders.

How he wished he had known his great grandfather. Montezuma's rule had been his great grandfather's legacy. He wondered often whether he could carry on his great grandfather's vision as he carried his name.

While Montezuma's thoughts wandered, his servant entered. "Strangers are reported near the city, my great emperor. They come in unusual dress and do not look like the people of these lands."

"Where are they?" Montezuma asked, still looking out his window.

"To the north, my lord. Two days at least."

"Do they carry weapons?" Montezuma had been dreaming of his great grandfather often, and in his visions great warnings came regarding men from foreign lands. The men carried weapons he had never seen. They caused great destruction.

"Yes, my lord. They have powerful weapons. They also have with them some warriors from neighboring people."

7. What is this story mostly about?
   A. an emperor who finds out about strangers coming to his kingdom
   B. a servant who meets strangers and brings them to his kingdom
   C. some visitors who come to a strange land to meet Montezuma
   D. an emperor's great grandfather and his military victories

8. If this story continued, what would probably be the main idea of the rest of the story?
   A. Montezuma welcomes the strangers and invites them to stay.
   B. The strangers come to make a peace treaty with Montezuma.
   C. Montezuma goes to war and loses his empire to the strangers.
   D. Montezuma and his great grandfather speak to the strangers.

9. What important idea in the story is shown by the words, "They also have with them some warriors from neighboring people"?
   A. The strangers come for a peaceful visit.
   B. The neighboring tribes have joined the strangers to fight.
   C. The strangers have made friends among other people.
   D. The tribes want to talk to Montezuma.

For three summers in a row, Lynn had planted several tomato plants in the shade near her garage, but none had produced fruit. After checking out a book on the subject, Lynn learned that tomato plants need plenty of sunlight, frequent watering, and cage-like supports to help them stand. "This year," Lynn thought, "I'll have more tomatoes than I ever dreamed of."

10. What will Lynn do with her tomato plants this year?
  A. move her garage somewhere else
  B. give them very little water
  C. plant them in a sunny location
  D. put them in cages in the house

Davida was planning a birthday party for her best friend, Marni. Davida called twelve of their friends and told them about the event. On Friday, May 12th, everyone would meet at Davida's house and hide in the basement. Marni would arrive a little later because Davida had suggested that the two of them watch a movie and eat some pizza. It had been two weeks since Davida contacted everyone, and everything seemed to be going according to plan.

11. How do you know the party is supposed to be a surprise?
  A. the friends are going to hide in the basement
  B. Davida called and told twelve friends about it
  C. everything seemed to be going according to plan
  D. for two weeks everyone was able to keep quiet

Every August, Ethan goes to summer camp. The camp is in the mountains near Yosemite National Park. It is also a six-and-a-half hour car trip from home. The last hour of the trip is always the worst for Ethan. The steep and narrow mountain roads twist and turn, making him feel queasy. Once he gets out of the car, however, he feels much better. The discomfort in his belly becomes a distant memory.

12. How will Ethan feel just before he gets to camp this summer?
  A. ready for vacation
  B. tired of driving
  C. excited about camp
  D. sick to his stomach

Kevin's parents got out of the car and walked toward the school's baseball field. Today was the first game of the season, and Kevin was one of the star players. Kevin's father carried an umbrella because the sky was dark and threatened rain. Kevin waved from across the field. Waving back, his parents sat down in the bleachers. But Kevin's father stood right back up. He turned and looked with dismay at the puddle on his seat.

13. What caused Kevin's father to get wet?
   A. being caught in the rain
   B. watching a baseball game
   C. sitting in some water
   D. forgetting his umbrella

Mira's old dresser was a piece of furniture that had been used to store her baby clothes. Mira needed something bigger now, something more grown-up. On Saturday, Mira's dad saw an interesting advertisement in the newspaper. A furniture store called Kempke's was having its annual year-end sale. He showed the advertisement to Mira and suggested they go look for a dresser. Mira was at the door and ready to go in an instant.

14. Mira and her dad are going to Kemke's because
   A. Mira saw a dresser there that she liked
   B. Mira needs to purchase a new dresser
   C. Mira enjoys going to sales with her dad
   D. Mira asked if they could go shopping

"It's time to get up, boys," repeated Stephan's mother. She was standing on the deck where Stephan and his five buddies had spent the night. The boys had come over to celebrate Stephan's birthday. They had ordered pizza, watched a movie, and slept under the stars. Stephan's mother had checked on them a couple of times during the night and found them giggling and goofing around. Now that it was day, they were sleepy and bleary-eyed.

15. What effect did staying up all night have on Stephen and his buddies?
   A. They forgot where they were.
   B. They saved the movie for later.
   C. They learned about the stars.
   D. They found it difficult to get up.

Whenever there was a problem to be solved, Arthur Fry had a solution. Growing up in a small Iowa town, Fry showed early signs of clever thinking. Out of some old lumber scraps, he created custom sleds that sped down snowy hillsides like no store-bought sled could.

Inventing wasn't Fry's only interest, however. He also loved singing and was a member of the church choir. It was while singing that Fry came across a problem that begged to be solved. In choir, Fry marked different parts of the songs he sang with tiny slips of paper. Every time he sat or turned a page, these carefully placed bookmarks fell out, and Fry lost his place. He puzzled over a way to make his bookmarks stick without hurting the pages of his songbook.

As it turned out, someone at the company where Fry worked had a sticky solution to his problem. Another chemist named Dr. Spencer Silver had invented a glue that did not dry but stayed soft and tacky. When this glue was put between two pieces of paper, they could be pulled apart without damaging the paper in any way.

Fry's need for sticky bookmarks and Silver's special glue came together to become the wildly popular product called Post-it Notes®. In 1981, Post-it Notes® were named 3M's best new product of the year. Today, Post-it NotesÆ come in different colors and sizes. Many people say they could not survive without these wonderful, sticky markers.

16. Which of these is a fact from the story?
A. Arthur Fry was a good singer.
B. Arthur Fry grew up in Iowa.
C. Arthur Fry created a new glue.
D. Arthur Fry collected bookmarks.

17. Which of these opinions can be inferred from the story?
A. Dr. Silver thought his glue was a failure.
B. Arthur Fry is one of America's best inventors.
C. Post-it Notes are used in many different ways.
D. Dr. Silver was Fry's best friend.

18. Which of these is an opinion about Post-it Notes?
A. They are made using Dr. Silver's glue.
B. They were 3M's best new product in 1981.
C. They come in different colors and sizes.
D. They are a wildly popular product.

Name _____ Date _____

Trent Montel will soon be the best skydiver in the state. Last year, he took second place at the state skydiving competition. This year, Montel plans to out-shine last year's champion. He has worked hard to improve his stunts. If he can prove his skill, he will probably take first place.

19. Which of these is a fact from the paragraph?
   A. Montel will soon be the best skydiver in the state.
   B. Montel took second place at last year's competition.
   C. Montel has improved his stunts and proven his skill.
   D. Montel will take first place at this year's competition.

The Wilshire Neighborhood Association wants to put speed bumps on Fremont Avenue. Construction for the project will cost $500 per speed bump. Supporters say that speed bumps will help to slow down traffic, making Fremont a more pleasant place for pedestrians. The rest of the neighborhood is not convinced. They worry that the speed bumps will make the street traffic seem even worse.

20. It is a fact that the speed bumps will
   A. make Fremont a pleasant place
   B. make traffic seem even worse
   C. slow down traffic
   D. cost $500 each

Lake Louise is part of Banff National Park in southern Alberta, Canada. The lake is about a mile and a half long and a third of a mile wide. Visitors find it quiet and peaceful at Lake Louise. The smooth waters mirror the surrounding mountains, creating breathtaking view. More people visit Lake Louise than anywhere else in the Canadian Rockies.

21. Which of these can be inferred from the paragraph?
   A. Lake Louise is close to the United States.
   B. People enjoy the spectacular scenery at Lake Louise.
   C. Lake Louise is the largest lake in Canada.
   D. The Canadian Rockies have many beautiful lakes.

Encyclopedia Article

The word *arena* comes from the Latin word *harena*, meaning sand. The ancient Romans built many amphitheaters for combats and other athletic competitions. Roman sports tended to be violent, so the center of the amphitheaters where the action took place was often covered with sand. The sand helped to soak up the blood so that the competitors wouldn't loose their footing. Eventually the word *harena* came to mean the area at the center of an amphitheater or stadium. In the seventeenth century, people speaking English began to use the word *arena* to describe the location of English sporting events.

Dictionary Entry [Have the pronunciation set using phonetic symbols.]

a-re-na (ə rē′ nə) *n*. 1. a central area used for sports or other forms of entertainment and surrounded by seats for spectators. 2. a field of competition or activity.

Newspaper Editorial

Patrons attending sporting events at modern arenas probably do not realize just how appropriate the word *arena* is. The original arenas were home to the bloody competitions of Roman gladiators. Today's arenas host violent professional sports competitions. Football, wrestling, hockey, and boxing are among the most violent of modern sports. Even athletes in "non-contact" sports often abandon the game to fight with opponents. This use of violence for entertainment may have its roots in ancient history, but it is dangerous to modern society. Not only are athletes themselves violent, but spectators may become dangerous mobs after witnessing the brutal competitions.

22. Which information source gives the most complete information about arenas?
  A. the newspaper editorial
  B. the dictionary entry
  C. the encyclopedia article
  D. They all give about the same information.

23. Which of these best describes the newspaper editorial's description of arenas?
  A. It is mostly fact.
  B. It contains many opinions.
  C. It shows that arenas are useful buildings.
  D. It is easier to understand than the other sources.

24. If you were writing a report for school, why would the information in the dictionary be least useful?
  A. It is short, and short things are never useful.
  B. It has fewer details about arenas than other sources.
  C. It gives two different definitions.
  D. It tells you how to pronounce *arena*.

Many early civilizations had successful mail systems. Ancient Persia, the home of a great civilization and center of a huge empire, is one example. The early Persians were nomads, or travelers, who settled the area about 1000 BCE. They were an organized people who developed a "pony express" type of mail-delivery service. Government workers were usually the only ones to use the service. Others had little need for mail, since few people could read or write.

25. Which of these statements is supported by the paragraph?
  A. Persians got their mail from visiting travelers.
  B. Government workers in Persia could read and write.
  C. Persia was the very first civilization to have mail.
  D. Government workers were more organized than most people.

The longest river in the United States is the Missouri River. From its start at the Jefferson River in southwestern Montana to its end at the Mississippi River just north of St. Louis, Missouri, the Missouri River covers 2,540 miles. The Missouri carries large amounts of dirt in its water. Farmers have described the Missouri River as "too thick to drink and too thin to plow."

26. Which words from this paragraph are meant to be humorous?
  A. "its start at the Jefferson River"
  B. "just north of St. Louis, Missouri"
  C. "large amounts of dirt in its water"
  D. "too thick to drink and too thin to plow"

The Golden Gate Bridge is one of the largest and most beautiful bridges in the world today. The bridge spans the San Francisco Bay, connecting northern California to the peninsula of San Francisco. The Golden Gate is a suspension bridge, with towers that hold up thick cables from which the bridge hangs. The floor of the bridge spans about 6,440 feet, is 90 feet wide, and rises 220 feet above the water. A six-lane road on the bridge is bordered with sidewalks. The bridge's towers, which often peek up through a blanket fog, are a symbol of the San Francisco Bay Area.

27. What can you conclude about the Golden Gate Bridge and support with evidence from the paragraph?
  A. Pedestrians are able to walk across it.
  B. It has the longest span of any other suspension bridge.
  C. Thinner cables would not be earthquake proof.
  D. It is the most popular bridge in the Bay Area.

Luxury Furniture is holding a once-in-a-lifetime sale. The popular furniture store is moving to a larger location in order to meet the needs of our customers. To celebrate the move, Luxury Furniture is giving away everything in their current warehouse. The owners of the store do not want to pay $500 to have someone move the thousands of pieces of furniture across town. As a solution, they have decided to give it all away.

28. Why is this information so difficult to believe?
    A. Many sales are called once-in-a-lifetime sales, so this sale is no different from any others.
    B. It doesn't sound like the furniture at Luxury Furniture is made very well.
    C. By giving everything away to avoid paying moving costs, the owners are losing even more money.
    D. A popular store that wants to meet customer demand would not need to move to a bigger location.

In China, the world's largest dam is being built across the Yangtze River in an area called the Three Gorges. Some people believe the dam is necessary to provide power for the area's growing demands. Others think the dam will be an environmental disaster for the Three Gorges, China's version of the Grand Canyon. Although the dam was started in 1994 and will not be finished until 2009, people still wonder whether or not building the dam is a good idea.

29. Which of these statements about the passage is most likely to be true?
    A. The Yangtze River is made up of three different rivers.
    B. The biggest dam in the world is under construction.
    C. The dam will supply all of the power the area needs.
    D. The dam will cause an environmental disaster.

Kim and Ty Vesta have taken a number of classes on how to speak Italian. One of their assignments was to go to an Italian restaurant and order in Italian. Last fall, they hosted a student from Italy for a period of three months. While the student stayed with the Vestas, they spoke only Italian during mealtime. The Vestas are now excited about planning a trip to Italy.

30. Which statement from the paragraph leads you to believe the Vestas can speak Italian fairly well?
    A. They have taken Italian classes.
    B. They hosted an Italian student.
    C. They are planning a trip to Italy.
    D. They spoke Italian during meals.

If you ask some people, the George Lucas of 800 BCE was an Ancient Greek poet named Homer. And the *Star Wars* and The *Empire Strikes Back* of that time were Homer's poems, the *Iliad* and the *Odyssey*.

People who study history know almost nothing about Homer. They aren't even positive he wrote the famous poems. According to tradition, he was a blind poet. Although that might not sound very impressive, it was. Anytime there was a royal feast or festival, the best poets or singing bards were called upon.

Homer probably entertained the crowd by reciting his poems. These weren't just ordinary poems; these were epic poems. Epic poems were not written down—not in Homer's time. The poems told well-known stories of famous heroes and great battles. Epic poems were so long that they had to be told in sections rather than all at once. Homer probably sat among the royalty, and with the aid of a simple harp, sang or recited segments from his epic poems.

The *Iliad* and the *Odyssey* are the only Greek epic poems that survived, probably because of their length and excellent quality. The poems describe the events during and after the legendary Trojan War, a war waged between Greece and Troy.

After Homer's time, the *Iliad* and the *Odyssey* were recited at Greek festivals and used to teach Greek children how to read. Many of Greece's later writers looked to Homer's work for their own inspiration.

31. Based in the information in this passage, you can tell that
A. Homer had a beautiful singing voice
B. poets were honored members of society
C. the Greeks were the first to have poetry
D. people fell asleep during epic poems

32. Since the *Iliad* and the *Odyssey* were later used to teach reading, they must have been
A. just for children
B. made shorter
C. written down
D. very funny

33. This passage supports the generalization that
A. people from all periods of history enjoy stories
B. the best way to become famous is to write a poem
C. stories provide us with information about the past
D. every poem that was ever written tells a story

Why wait for excitement to come to your doorstep? With Party Lights, your doorstep will be the excitement. You'll be the talk of the neighborhood with these decorative hanging lights. Party Lights will make your home more fun and make your family life more exciting. Guests of all ages will love the elegant and attractive lights. Party Lights have different settings for your different moods. They can flash when you want a glitzy party feeling. They can also be set on low glow to add romance to your entry or door. Party Lights can even be set to blink to your favorite music! So whether you're hosting a party or just looking to add a little flavor to your life, Party Lights are just what you need.

34. Which of these is an example of incorrect thinking in the passage?
   A. Party Lights can be used to set different moods.
   B. Party Lights are elegant, glitzy, and attractive.
   C. Party Lights make your family life more exciting.
   D. Party Lights can blink to your favorite music.

Dear Editor,
The article written on February 2 made me very upset. The writer said that the boys' soccer team could not win without Sean Garza, who was injured Monday. Sean Garza has led the team in scoring this season. In fact, only two other players have scored points in our six games. Those points were scored with assists by Sean. Sean is the team's captain and helps the coach make important decisions about plays. But this doesn't mean that the team won't be able to win without him.

35. In the passage, the author says that the soccer team can win without Sean Garza. How does the author support this inference?
   A. Garza has led the tem in scoring this season.
   B. Garza has assisted other players in scoring.
   C. Garza has helped the coach make decisions.
   D. The author does not support the inference in the passage.

The Park Action Commission (PAC) was started in 1979 to make sure that parks and wildlife were protected. We have been supported by private donations since we began. Many parks were in danger of becoming littered beyond help, and local wildlife were eating things like plastic bags and aluminum foil left by guests. PAC has improved the national parks and kept animals safe for over 20 years. We ask the state of Montana to consider giving us money so that we can keep doing the job we do. Without PAC's help, Montana's parks would not be receiving so many visitors and its wildlife would not be thriving. Help PAC to help you by funding our projects this year.

36. Which of these is an example of persuasion from the passage?
   A. Help PAC to help you by funding our projects this year.
   B. Wildlife were eating plastic bags and aluminum foil left by park guests.
   C. PAC was started in 1979 to make sure parks and wildlife were protected.
   D. We have been supported by private donations since we began.

Sharks are the most dangerous of predators. They live in oceans throughout the world but are the most common in warm waters. The whale shark is the largest species of shark and may grow up to 40 feet. The smallest grow to a mere six inches long. Most sharks eat their prey whole or tear off bite-sized pieces. Sharks have a reputation for attacking humans, and about 100 attacks are reported each year.

37. Why is the author's statement that sharks are the most dangerous of predators probably wrong?
  A. The author doesn't explain how sharks eat.
  B. The author doesn't mention anything about the shark's multiple rows of teeth.
  C. The author doesn't explain what kinds of sharks are dangerous.
  D. The author doesn't compare sharks to other predators.

Virginia Hamilton is considered one of today's most popular children's book authors. Her novels, folktales, and nonfiction writings tell imaginative stories about the heritage of African-Americans. Hamilton, whose books sell in the hundreds of thousands, won the 1975 Newbery Medal and the 1975 National Book Award for *M.C. Higgins, the Great.* Winning the Newbery was especially sweet for Hamilton because she was the first African-American to receive the award.

38. Which of these is the most important evidence that Virginia Hamilton is a popular author?
  A. She writes good books that lots of children enjoy.
  B. Her books sell hundreds of thousands of copies.
  C. Her stories are imaginative.
  D. She received a Newbery Medal.

Mount Everest is the highest mountain in the world. Located along the borders of Nepal and Tibet, it is one of the most difficult mountains on earth to climb.

39. Which of these is the best support for the opinion that Mount Everest is one of the most difficult mountains on earth to climb?
  A. It wasn't until 1975 that the first woman, Junko Tabei of Japan, reached the top of the mountain.
  B. People who have measured the mountain agree it is the highest mountain but disagree about its exact height.
  C. The mountain is extremely steep and has frequent avalanches, strong winds, and air that has little oxygen.
  D. Some Nepalese climbers believe that a creature called a Yeti, or Abominable Snowman, lives around Everest.

Recently, some parents tried to remove *The Wizard Walks* from the shelves of the local public library. These foolish people are entitled to decide for themselves what they will read, but *The Wizard Walks* should not be banned.

The people who object to *The Wizard Walks* believe that it is unsuitable for children. However, a poll showed that most people who want to ban *The Wizard Walks* haven't even read the book. I am offended by their attempt to ban *The Wizard Walks*. They are mindlessly repeating what they have heard from others without taking the trouble to research the subject themselves.

The main argument for banning *The Wizard Walks* is that it is almost a textbook on magic. But anyone who has actually read *The Wizard Walks* knows that it does not teach witchcraft. Although the main character of *The Wizard Walks* has magical powers, the story is obviously fictional. Most children have no trouble figuring out that *The Wizard Walks* describes an imaginary world.

Perhaps *The Wizard Walks* is not good for every child, but banning it from the public libraries goes too far. If ignorant people start banning books, soon the libraries will be empty. Every book is offensive to someone for some reason.

Parents who do not want children to read *The Wizard Walks* can ban it from their homes. To ban if from the public library would take away the right of other parents to make that decision for their own children.

40. Why is the author offended by the attempt to ban *The Wizard Walks*?
  A. Many supporters of the ban have not read the book.
  B. The author used *The Wizard Walks* to learn witchcraft.
  C. The author enjoyed reading *The Wizard Walks* very much.
  D. Supporters of the ban are prejudiced against witchcraft.

41. There is enough evidence in this essay to show that the author believes
  A. only a few books should ever be banned from the library
  B. all children should be required to read The Wizard Walks
  C. *The Wizard Walks* is the best children's book of our time
  D. public libraries should have a wide variety of books

42. Which of these is the first clue that the author does not respect the supporters of the ban?
  A. The author calls the supporters "foolish people."
  B. The author says the supporters are acting "mindlessly."
  C. The author says the book is "not good" for all children.
  D. The author suggests parents "ban it from their homes."

Students who break school rules still belong in school. The practice of suspending rule-breaking students does not prevent future problems. When these students return to school, they are behind in their schoolwork. Often they immediately get into more trouble. Troublemakers need more supervision than other students, not less. But when students are kicked out of school, they are free to roam the community and commit serious crimes. Troublemakers do not want to be in school anyway, so suspensions simply give them what they want.

43. Which of the following is the <u>weakest</u> support for the belief that students should not be suspended?
  A. Troublemakers need more supervision than other students.
  B. Suspensions do not keep students out of trouble.
  C. Troublemakers do not see suspensions as punishments.
  D. Suspended students fall behind in their classes.

Skateboarding should be confined to skating parks. Although I have never seen an accident happen to a skateboarder, I can easily imagine one. Skateboarders often travel at high speeds and they could easily knock over pedestrians. While skateboarding is fun and it is good exercise, it should not be done on city streets and sidewalks. There are plenty of areas in the city's parks where skateboarders can safely enjoy themselves.

44. How does the author support the argument that skateboarding should only be allowed in skating parks?
  A. Skateboarders often hit people on sidewalks.
  B. Skateboarders need to get more exercise.
  C. Skateboarders do not belong on the street.
  D. The author does not support the argument.

The *Standard Examiner* will no longer print any letters to the editor that are sent in by e-mail. Anyone wishing to express an opinion should take the time to sit down and write a letter. *Standard Examiner* receives too many e-mail messages each week for the staff to handle, and most of them are simply ridiculous. Instead of making calm, well-reasoned arguments, these e-mail messages are filled with biased, unsupported opinions.

45. There is enough information in this passage to show that the staff of the *Standard Examiner*
  A. receives letters complaining about the use of e-mail
  B. believes letters are better than e-mail messages
  C. carefully reads each e-mail message it receives
  D. enjoys getting responses of any kind from its readers

Mastery Tests
Reading Comprehension:
Locating and Using Information

Directions for all questions in this test:

Read each passage and answer the questions that follow it. Some items will have no passage. On the answer sheet, fill in the bubble for the answer you think is correct.

Sample Questions:

To use your digital wireless phone, first press the POWER button. This activates the phone. Next, dial the number you want to call. As you touch the number buttons, the digits will appear on the LCD screen. When you have finished dialing, press the SEND button. At the completion of your call, press the END button. To recall a stored number and dial it automatically, press RECALL. Use the up and down arrows to scroll among the numbers. Press SELECT to dial the number that is highlighted.

---

1. If you want to dial a stored number automatically, what button should you press after the phone has been activated?
   A. END
   B. SEND
   C. POWER
   D. RECALL

2. Which of these is the best description of what the LCD screen does?
   A. It dials the phone.
   B. It shows information.
   C. It shows if the phone is on or off.
   D. It selects a number.

MegaMaze is a game designed for use on Macintosh computers only. If you do not have a Macintosh computer, you will have to order PCMegaMaze. You must have 16 megabytes (MB) of RAM, 45 MB of available hard disk space, a 4X CD-ROM drive, and Mac OS 7.6 or higher to install and play MegaMaze.

To ensure that you don't have any problems installing or using MegaMaze, take the following precautions before you begin installation. First, check to make sure that your computer has the necessary system requirements. Second, shut down all virus-protection programs so they will not interfere with the installation of MegaMaze. (After you install MegaMaze, you can turn them on again.) Last, close any programs you have running on your computer.

To install MegaMaze, put the MegaMaze CD-ROM in the CD-ROM drive. The MegaMaze installation window will then appear on the Macintosh desktop. In the MegaMaze installation window, double-click on the icon labeled "MegaMaze Installer." In the MegaMaze Installer dialog box, click on the icon labeled "Install." Then, simply follow the on-screen instructions to complete the installation of MegaMaze.

If you have any questions about installing MegaMaze on your computer, you can call the Giant Games help-line during normal business hours at 1-800-555-4328. However, we recommend that you first visit the MegaMaze section of the Giant Games web site. You can find the answers to many frequently asked questions posted at our web site. The address is: www.giantgames.com/products/megamaze/mac.html.

To begin playing MegaMaze, find the MegaMaze folder on your hard drive. Then, double-click on the MegaMaze folder. After the folder opens, double-click on the MegaMaze icon. When the "Enter the Maze" screen appears, click on the button labeled "Name Your Traveler" and then begin your journey through the maze. If want to continue playing with a traveler from an earlier journey, click on the button labeled "Existing Travelers."

1. What should you do if you want to play MegaMaze using a traveler from an earlier journey?
   A. Click on the button labeled "Existing Travelers."
   B. Click on the button labeled "Name Your Traveler."
   C. Find the "Earlier Travels" file in the MegaMaze folder.
   D. Install an earlier version of MegaMaze on your computer.

2. What should you do right after you click on the icon labeled "Install"?
   A. Visit the Giant Games web site for help.
   B. Double-click on the "MegaMaze Installer" icon.
   C. Turn off the computer and start over again.
   D. Follow the instructions that appear on the screen.

3. Why is it important to shut down virus-protection software before installing MegaMaze?
   A. MegaMaze needs the hard disk space used by the virus-protection software.
   B. The virus-protection software might interfere with MegaMaze.
   C. Installing MegaMaze might damage the virus-protection software.
   D. Giant Games promises that MegaMaze CD-ROMs do not carry any viruses.

Tapestry Theater Presents Its
Sixth Annual Summer Workshops
July 10–14 For Grades 6–8

Attendance Fee: $50 for the whole week or $15 for one day
Location: Tapestry Theater Co-op on Southwest Broadway
Drama Workshop Choices:
     1. Comedy 2. Tragedy 3. Romance 4. Mystery 5. History

1. Name: _____(Please Print)

2. Address: _____

_____

3. Telephone: _____

4. Gender: M   F

5. Your grade level next fall: _____

6. Workshop first choice: 1 2 3 4 5 (Circle one)

7. Workshop second choice: 1 2 3 4 5

8. Signature: _____

If under 18, a parent's signature is required.

To ensure enrollment in the workshop(s) of your choice, complete this form and mail it with a check before July 1st to Tapestry Theater Co-op, 1104 Southwest Broadway. Late enrollment is permitted, but there is no guarantee that workshops will be available at that time.

---

4. Which information goes on line 5?
  A. how old you are that summer
  B. your grade level in the fall
  C. the year that you were born
  D. which workshops you prefer

5. If you mail the form and a check after July 1st, what might happen?
  A. You might not know where the theater is.
  B. You will not be allowed to participate.
  C. You may not get the workshops you want.
  D. You will have to pay a small late fee.

6. How would you probably complete line 7?
  A. Print the workshop's name.
  B. Circle your choice.
  C. Circle your grade level.
  D. Sign your name.

The Chef's Gourmet Hand Mixer is designed to help you prepare many delicious foods. Please read all instructions and safety tips before using your Chef's Gourmet Hand Mixer.

Using Your Hand Mixer:
Before using your mixer for the first time, wash the beaters and the mixing bowl. Be sure that the speed control is in the OFF position and the mixer is not plugged in. Insert the beaters one at a time into the opening on the bottom of the mixer. Push in until the beater clicks into position. Then, plug the cord into a standard household electrical outlet (120 volt, 60 Hz A.C.).

Mixing:
Slowly move the mixer around the bowl. When adding ingredients, turn the speed control to OFF and rest the mixer on its heel. Be sure to place the beaters so that any drippings will fall back into the bowl.

When you are done mixing, set the speed control to **1** and raise the beaters slowly from the batter to clean off any clinging food. Be sure to turn the control to OFF before raising the beaters completely out of the bowl. When you wish to wash the beaters, press the EJECT button to release the beaters into the sink.

7. What should you do just before inserting the beaters?
A. Connect the mixer to an outlet.
B. Turn off and unplug the mixer.
C. Set the speed control to 1.
D. Rock the mixer back onto its heel.

8. What does the EJECT button allow you to do?
A. Clean the food from the beaters.
B. Lift the mixer from the mixing bowl.
C. Change the speed control setting.
D. Remove the beaters from the mixer.

9. When adding ingredients, you should position the beaters over the mixing bowl so that
A. any food on the beaters will drip into the bowl.
B. the beaters and mixer will be out of your way.
C. you can easily scrape down the sides of the bowl.
D. new ingredients will fall directly onto the beaters.

Although many people don't even know his name, Earle Dickson was responsible for creating one of today's most common household items. Dickson was the genius behind Band-Aids®.

In 1917, Dickson was a newly married man and a cotton buyer for a successful bandage company in New Jersey called Johnson & Johnson.

As the story goes, Dickson's wife, Frances, was accident-prone. She often cut herself or nicked her fingers doing various household tasks. The regular bandages were too big and clumsy for Frances, so Dickson devised something better.

He folded pads of cotton gauze and placed them on long strips of surgical tape. He covered this with a material called crinoline. This prevented the tape from sticking to itself when it was rolled back together. Frances could unroll the bandage and cut off as much as she needed.

One day, Dickson mentioned his creation to a friend at work. Soon, Dickson was before the Johnsons, showing them what he had come up with. The Johnsons were especially impressed with the fact that you could put the new bandage on yourself. Up until that point, bandages had been difficult to apply without help.

Johnson & Johnson began producing Band-Aids, but the bandages didn't take off until the mid-1920s when the company gave thousands of samples to the Boy Scouts. After that, Band-Aids were a hit. Dickson was made vice president of Johnson & Johnson, and when he died in 1961, the company was selling $30,000,000 dollars' worth of Band-Aids a year.

10. Here is an outline of the passage.

The Invention of Band-Aids

I. Who Earle Dickson was

II. _____

III. How Dickson made his own bandage

IV. What happened at Johnson & Johnson

V. The success of Band-Aids

Which answer would fit best in the blank in the outline?

A. Where Johnson & Johnson was

B. What Dickson's wife's name was

C. Why Dickson made his own bandage

D. How Dickson met with Johnson & Johnson

11. If you were taking notes about this passage, which of these would *not* belong?

A. Dickson became vice president

B. Band-Aids were popular right away

C. Early bandages were difficult to put on

D. Dickson worked for Johnson & Johnson

12. Which of these is the best summary of the passage?

A. The Boy Scouts made Band-Aids more popular.

B. A housewife is finally able to bandage herself.

C. A cotton inventor becomes head of a company.

D. One man's homemade bandages become Band-Aids.

Mastery Test
Literary Response and Analysis
Structural Features

Directions for all questions in this test:

Read each passage and answer the questions that follow it. Some items will have no passage. On the answer sheet, fill in the bubble for the answer you think is correct.

Sample Question:

1. A play about an English king is an example of
   A. fiction.
   B. nonfiction.
   C. drama.
   D. poetry.

1. A fantasy story would probably be about
   A. why the dinosaurs disappeared.
   B. the life of a real queen.
   C. a mouse who saved a lion.
   D. an imaginary world.

2. Which of these probably came from a myth?
   A. Atlantis was said to exist long ago and contained an advanced civilization.
   B. Ulysses S. Grant had been unsuccessful at almost everything he had tried.
   C. Flying across the ocean alone was an enormous challenge that had cost several people their lives.
   D. The great bear stood on its back legs, sniffed the air, and then turned and walked into the forest.

3. The miners talked about the place where nuggets of gold as big as a man's hand were just lying on the ground, waiting to be picked up. This story would be considered
   A. science fiction .
   B. a legend.
   C. historic fiction.
   D. a fairy tale.

4. Which of these is true about fables?
   A. They are about places and things that do not exist.
   B. They are about true events exactly as they happened.
   C. They are often partially true but exaggerated.
   D. They are often about animals and teach lessons.

5. Which of these is a characteristic of poetry?
   A. Characters' thoughts are told, making them seem real.
   B. The words that are chosen create rhythm and rhyme.
   C. Characters' parts are read aloud.
   D. Events are listed in the order that they happened.

6. How is drama different from other kinds of literature?
   A. It is meant to be read as well as acted out.
   B. It has characters that seem like real people.
   C. It ends each line with a word that rhymes.
   D. It has a setting where the story takes place.

7. What is an advantage of writing nonfiction?
   A. You can create as many characters as you want.
   B. You can write using mostly your imagination.
   C. You can leave some of the punctuation out.
   D. You can focus on telling just the facts.

8. Which of these is true about fiction?
   A. It explains how to do or make something
   B. It has a unique rhythm to its lines.
   C. It makes true stories more interesting.
   D. It has no limit to what it can be about.

9. Which of these tells how legend is different from fantasy?
   A. Legend is pure fiction and is rarely based on real events.
   B. Legend is often handed down as part of a people's tradition.
   C. Legend is best known for its clever use of surprise endings.
   D. Legend is a form of literature that makes animals seem human.

10. What could happen in a piece of historic fiction?
    A. Animals speak and behave as though they are human.
    B. Scientific events from the future are predicted.
    C. Real people from centuries ago speak their minds.
    D. A made-up character learns a lesson from a dragon.

11. Which of these is true about a work of drama?
    A. It is a long story that is never written down. It is handed down from one generation of people to the next.
    B. It is a made-up story that often includes animals and teaches a valuable life lesson.
    C. It is a true story about a historic event from long ago. It often uses rhyme to get its meaning across.
    D. It is a story that is performed by a group of people, often on a stage before an audience.

12. Which of these probably came from a book of realistic fiction?
    A. The creature had three eyes and stared at its reflection in a mirror.
    B. Hector had to return home because he'd forgotten his favorite umbrella.
    C. The silver space ship was touching down in the middle of my backyard.
    D. If Janet listened carefully, she could understand what the birds were saying.

13. Which of these characters would be considered a myth?
    A. Betsy Ross, who made the first American flag
    B. Cleopatra, who ruled Egypt long ago
    C. Aphrodite, a Greek goddess
    D. Queen Elizabeth, the daughter of Henry VIII

The United States has often been called a "melting pot" of peoples and cultures. It is true that the country is one of the most ethnically diverse societies in the world. Still, the name "melting pot" might not describe today's reality. Rather than everyone melting into a single, unified culture, many Americans work hard to keep their particular cultural background alive and distinct.

14. This paragraph can best be described as
   A. an editorial saying that the United States really is a "melting pot."
   B. a short story about about a special culture.
   C. a novel that entertains the reader.
   D. an essay arguing against a point of view.

Suddenly, Vianne's shovel hit something hard, so she stooped down to take a look. The hard object appeared to be a box of some kind. Vianne carefully dug around the box and then lifted it from its hiding place behind the barn. Rubbing it clean with her sweatshirt sleeve, Vianne saw that the box was made of pure gold and was encrusted with diamonds, rubies, and sapphires. Her heart beat wildly as she lifted the lid.

15. Which of these best describes this paragraph?
   A. It compares life on a farm to life in a palace.
   B. It is the beginning of a story meant to persuade.
   C. It is part of a story meant to be read for enjoyment.
   D. It is like an encyclopedia entry about archaeologists.

16. Which of these would be the most likely topic for a short story?
   A. a trip down a trail in the Grand Canyon
   B. a description of the rock layers in the Grand Canyon
   C. an argument for expanding Grand Canyon National Park
   D. an explanation of how the Grand Canyon was formed

Mastery Test
Literary Response and Analysis
Narrative Analysis: Story Elements

Directions for all questions in this test:

Read each passage and answer the questions that follow it. Some items will have no passage. On the answer sheet, fill in the bubble for the answer you think is correct.

Sample Questions:

The winter had been colder than usual, and the river was still frozen solid. In a normal year, the thaw would have been well under way by now and the river would be flowing. Logs could be sent down to the mill, bringing much-needed money to the town. Mayor Haskins didn't know what to, but he was sure that Mrs. Romero would. Even though she was over 80 years old, her mind was razor sharp, and she would remember what people had done before in years like this.

---

1. The problem in this story is that
   A. the weather has been colder than usual.
   B. logs can't be sent down the river.
   C. the mayor doesn't have a solution.
   D. Mrs. Romero was over 80 years old.

2. The paragraph suggests that
   A. people like Mrs. Romero.
   B. the mayor is embarrassed he can't solve the problem.
   C. Mrs. Romero was once a logger.
   D. the mayor has confidence in Mrs. Romero.

The woman who changed nursing forever, Florence Nightingale, was raised in a well-to-do family in the mid-1800s. Her parents expected her to get married as soon as she found a husband, as most women in England did at the time. Her father was also committed to education and taught his daughters history, philosophy, Latin, Greek, and German, as well as other languages. Nightingale was a good student and eventually convinced her parents to allow her to study mathematics as well.

Nightingale believed her purpose in life was to be a nurse. Nursing at that time was not a respected profession. Women who were poor or had no other opportunity became nurses in those days. Hospitals had bad practices for keeping their buildings clean and free of germs. Nightingale's parents would not allow her to become a nurse, but she was persistent. She waited for their permission, never changing her mind. While she waited, she studied how hospitals were run and kept detailed notes of what she saw.

Her parents finally agreed to allow Florence to study nursing, but not in England. Her parents sent her to a school in Europe and hoped she would think twice about nursing.

In 1853 the Crimean War broke out, and British troops were sent to Turkey to fight. Reports came back that wounded soldiers were dying because of the poor hospital conditions. Florence had a friend in British politics who knew that she was just the person to help. He sent her and 38 other women to Turkey, where Florence cleaned up the military hospital. Her persistence paid off once again. The hospital was transformed from a rat-infested barracks with a high rate of infection to a clean place where men received proper care.

Nightingale spent only three years working as a nurse in Turkey. When she returned home, she was sick and felt uncomfortable being around other people. For the rest of her life, Nightingale fought to improve the British healthcare system through her writing. Nightingale changed the way hospitals took care of their sick and kept their buildings sanitary. She also helped nursing become a respectable profession in England.

1. Nightingale's parents allowed her to study nursing because
   A. the healthcare system in England improved.
   B. Nightingale had a hard time finding a husband.
   C. nurses were needed for war hospitals in Turkey.
   D. they saw her persistence and desire.

2. How did Nightingale help the British healthcare system after the war?
   A. She worked as a nurse until her death.
   B. She became a director of health care.
   C. She fought for change through her writing.
   D. She taught at a respected nursing school.

3. You can tell that Nightingale wanted to be a nurse because she
   A. studied on her own how hospitals were run.
   B. wanted to study math and was a good student.
   C. spent her life fighting to change the hospitals.
   D. came home from Turkey after only three years.

Margo and Fallon went to the old barn for the third day in a row. Quietly they slipped in through a cracked board on the side of the barn. There in the middle of the barn was a tiny ball of matted fur lapping up milk from the bowl sitting in front of him.

"He's drinking it!" Margo whispered with delight. The girls slowly moved forward. The kitten started. He looked up, saw the girls, and bolted up into the hayloft.

"He's too scared. He'll never trust us to take care of him," Margo said.

"I have one more idea. You wait here," said Fallon. She came back in a few minutes with a can of tuna. They took little pieces of tuna and made a path to where they were sitting. The kitten slowly began to follow the tuna trail. Finally he came cautiously near the girls. He sniffed and picked at each bite of tuna until he was eating out of their hands.

4. Why did the girls make a trail of tuna for the kitten?
   A. The kitten was supposed to be outside.
   B. They wanted the kitten to trust them.
   C. They wanted the kitten to like tuna.
   D. The kitten was hungry and needed food.

The hikers had walked for two hours before coming to the river. The place they wanted to camp was just on the other side. This time last year the river was only knee deep, and they had no trouble making it across. But the March rains had been worse than usual, and the river was now shoulder deep with a strong current.

"Any ideas?" the guide asked the campers. They all stood silent for a moment.

Finally, Quinn spoke up. "Maybe if we gather some branches, we could make a raft for our gear. If we tied a rope across the river, we could hold onto that while we crossed with our stuff."

They all agreed and gathered the materials they needed. Carefully they crossed one by one, while Quinn brought the raft back and forth for each camper.

5. How did making a raft solve the campers' problem?
   A. They were able to keep their gear dry while crossing the river.
   B. They crossed the river by sitting on the raft and paddling.
   C. They all swam across together by using the raft as a float.
   D. They could use the raft in case they had trouble crossing the river.

6. What is the main conflict of the story?
   A. Quinn is bossy and insists they use her solution.
   B. The hikers could not find a place to camp.
   C. There are no branches to make a raft.
   D. The chosen campsite is difficult to get to.

Going to the grocery store was simply no fun. Harold slumped on his bicycle and rode off with heavy sigh. There were a million other things he'd rather be doing.

At least there was a shortcut to Pedrini's. Harold swerved, turning down the back alley.

It was early June, and the Detroit neighborhood was alive with activity. Harold could hear the sounds of workers hammering nails. Giggles bubbled up from a yard where children played under a sprinkler. A pair of women chattered on a back porch.

Then Harold heard a strange sputtering. It sounded like a motor of some kind — and it was coming from Mr. Ford's back shed. Mr. Ford was always working on some new invention. The neighbors called him "Crazy Henry," but Harold thought Mr. Ford was a lot of fun.

As Harold approached the shed, he grew worried. The backside of the shed had a huge hole torn in it! Harold stopped his bike and peeked inside. "Hello?" he called nervously.

"Harold!" said Mr. Ford, emerging from the shadows. "Come take a look." Harold leaned his bike against the fence and stepped inside. His mouth instantly dropped.

"It's an automobile," said Mr. Ford. "I finished it this morning. The darn thing had so much get-up-and-go, it took out my back wall," he said, chuckling.

"Can we go for a ride?" breathed Harold excitedly.

Mr. Ford grinned. "You bet," he said.

Harold glanced at this watch. He wanted to remember this moment. At exactly 3:30 in the afternoon on June 4th, 1896, he had gone for a ride in the first automobile Henry Ford ever made.

---

7. Why did the writer begin this story by making Harold wish he were doing something else?
 A. to make the town of Detroit seem boring
 B. to make the story longer
 C. to make the later events seem more exciting
 D. to make the other characters seem uncaring

8. Which words does the author use to create a sense of surprise over what is in the shed?
 A. "The neighbors called him 'Crazy Henry.' . . ."
 B. "The darn thing had so much get-up-and-go. . . ."
 C. "A pair of women chattered . . . ."
 D. "His mouth instantly dropped."

9. What is the purpose of the last paragraph of the story?
 A. It explains who Mr. Ford really was.
 B. It shows that the story is based on real events.
 C. It helps the reader imagine the city of Detroit.
 D. It tells why Henry forgot to go to the butcher shop.

> Marilee and Chenda crouched behind the sofa. They glanced over at Clifton and Chris as the boys hid under the table and tried not to giggle. Mrs. Dwamena peeked out through the front shades and quickly whispered, "Okay, they're coming. Everyone be quiet!"
>
> They heard the door open and listened for Mrs. Dwamena's cue. "Surprise!" everyone shouted as they jumped out from their hiding places.

10. Why were Marilee and Chenda crouched behind the sofa?
   A. They were hiding from Clifton and Chris.
   B. Mrs. Dwamena was looking for them.
   C. They were trying to surprise someone.
   D. Mrs. Dwamena asked them to find something.

> "I don't know if I can stand this heat another day," Jaime said to Leo. The temperature had been 100 degrees for the first five days of camp. All of the camp activities were outside, and no water activities had been planned for the week. As the boys walked slowly away from the shade tree, they noticed that a group of boys was following Mr. Crier, the camp director. When they saw that he was holding some paddles and a plastic raft, they gave each other a high five and ran to follow him.

11. Why did the boys follow Mr. Crier?
   A. Mr. Crier needed help with an activity he was leading.
   B. They knew that Mr. Crier was starting a water activity.
   C. They wanted to help Mr. Crier carry the equipment.
   D. Mr. Crier asked the boys to follow him to the river.

> Isaac wanted to do something special for his mother, so he decided to make lasagna, her favorite dish. Laying out all the ingredients, Isaac checked to make sure he had everything the recipe called for.
>
> "Oh no!" Isaac said to himself. He thought for a moment, then grabbed a small bowl and dashed out the front door. Within minutes he was back from Mrs. Arnold's house carefully setting the bowl of eggs on the counter.

12. Why did Isaac go to Mrs. Arnold's house?
   A. He needed to borrow eggs for the lasagna.
   B. He asked her for a recipe for lasagna.
   C. Mrs. Arnold had a good recipe for lasagna.
   D. Mrs. Arnold made some lasagna for Isaac.

Read these three stories, and then answer the questions about them.

Long ago, a tortoise who wanted to become wise crept into the home of the gods. He hid in his shell so the gods believed he was a rock.

One day, when the gods were elsewhere, the tortoise stole the gourd holding all the wisdom in the world. He tied it around his neck and started home. Soon, a fallen tree blocked his way. The gourd around his neck kept him from climbing over it. The tortoise, having wisdom tied around his neck but little in his head, did not shift the gourd to his back.

Finally, the frustrated tortoise took the gourd from around his neck and threw it to the ground. It broke into many pieces, and since that day, wisdom has been scattered all over the earth.

Coyote secretly wished to view the earth from high above. One day, he challenged Raven. "You are so weak you could never lift an animal such as myself into the air."

Raven was eager to prove his strength, so he took hold of Coyote's thick, blue fur and lifted him into the air. Coyote marveled to see the earth below him. Then he boasted, "Raven, you are strong but not clever. I tricked you into helping me fly."

At that, Raven let go of Coyote's blue fur and Coyote fell to the earth far below. That is how Coyote's blue fur became the dusty brown and black of the earth.

No rain had fallen for months, and the animals grew thirsty. They worked for many hours digging a well. Hare said, "I will let them dig and then drink my fill."

After the well was dug, Hare yelled, "The King is behind the hill!" The animals went to see the King while Hare drank and washed his dusty body. The animals returned to find the water muddy. "Who did this? We must set a trap."

Around the well, they poured sticky sap and placed ropes. When Hare next came to drink, he tangled himself in the sap and ropes. At last, frightened by the binding ropes, he ran far from the well.

13. Which lesson is contained in all of these stories?
    A. Honest work is better than tricks.
    B. Careful planning is important.
    C. No one wants to be a thief's friend.
    D. Cleverness does not always pay.

14. How are all three characters alike?
    A. They all tricked others to get what they wanted.
    B. They all showed great wisdom and concern for others.
    C. They all were bossy and gave many orders to others.
    D. They all believed that honesty is important.

15. In which way is the first story different from the others?
    A. The tortoise needed wisdom more than Coyote needed to fly or Hare needed water.
    B. The tortoise is more successful in his trick than Coyote and Hare.
    C. The tortoise plans to share what he takes with the whole world.
    D. The tortoise did not suffer for his trick, but the Coyote and Hare did.

"Oh, Toni!" Alexis shouted after they crossed the Mississippi. "We're finally in Memphis! I can't wait to get to Gramma Ruthie's and see Kate."

Toni grinned. "Hellooooo Memphis!" she yelled out the window. Then she turned to her sister. "Boring cousin Kate? All she ever does is listen to the aunties gossip.

"It's not gossip!" Alexis insisted. "The aunties know all the family stories, going back over a hundred years. Kate and I are learning them. You're going to grow up not knowing anything about our family, Toni." Alexis shook her head in disapproval.

"I know the important part!" Toni answered back. "I know we're a blues family. Most of those stories are about the blues musicians in our family, aren't they? The music is more important than the stories."

"Why are you so happy to be in Memphis if you don't want to hear family stories?" asked Alexis.

"Uncle Raymond promised to take me down to Beale Street to listen to the live blues bands."

"Live music?" Alexis frowned. "I hate those places. People are so noisy you can hardly hear the music."

"Well, maybe you'll like it better when we come home from Beale Street. Didn't you notice what I put in my backpack?"

"Your harmonica? Are you really going get up and play that in front of everyone?"

"That's right," Toni said proudly, "and I heard Momma say that you're going to tell everyone the story you learned about Great-Uncle Albert and his trip to Chicago."

16. Toni thinks that Cousin Kate is boring because
   A. Kate tells stories about family musicians.
   B. Kate likes to listen to family stories.
   C. Kate lives in Memphis with Gramma Ruthie.
   D. Kate wants to go down to Beale Street.

17. Why is Toni probably so excited about listening to live blues bands?
   A. Toni enjoys being around noisy people.
   B. Toni wants to get away from Alexis.
   C. Toni likes Uncle Raymond.
   D. Toni is a musician herself.

18. Why does Alexis listen to her aunties tell stories?
   A. She wants to know her family's history.
   B. She has nothing else to do at Gramma Ruthie's.
   C. She likes it when the aunties gossip.
   D. She knows music is important to her family.

Jack leaned back and closed his eyes, enjoying the warm sun. He'd hadn't been too happy when Mrs. Morris asked him to baby-sit her two kids, but it wasn't too hard. In fact, he probably didn't even need to be here. After all, Lawrence was just running around the backyard, and Amy was picking strawberries from the garden. All Jack had to do was relax.

Suddenly, Lawrence screamed. Jack jumped up and saw that Amy was holding her throat and her face was bright red. It looked like she couldn't breathe.

Jack was really scared, but he tried to remember what he'd learned at a first-aid class a few years ago. All of a sudden, the words of the first-aid teacher popped into his head: "If you're going to help people, you have to stay calm."

Ok, Jack thought, I'll stay calm and think. I saw Amy eat a strawberry, and now she can't breathe. "She's choking," he shouted. "Lawrence, go call 911. Tell them Amy's choking."

Lawrence sprinted toward the house. Jack moved around behind Amy and wrapped his arms around her waist. Quickly, he pulled in as hard as he could. Amy made a coughing sound and spit out the strawberry. She took a shaky breath and started crying.

When Mrs. Morris came home, she thanked Jack over and over again. That didn't seem right to Jack. Finally he said, "Really, you shouldn't thank me. You should thank my first-aid teacher. If she hadn't taught me that the most important thing to do is to stay calm, I wouldn't have been able to remember how to help Amy."

19. Jack was not watching Lawrence and Amy closely because
  A. they were too far away from him.
  B. Mrs. Morris told him that he didn't have to.
  C. he didn't think they needed him.
  D. he was busy doing something else.

20. Which of these is probably true about Jack?
  A. He enjoys knowing how to help people.
  B. He panics when someone gets hurt.
  C. He likes spending time with younger kids.
  D. He often gets into trouble because he is lazy.

21. At the end of the story, you can tell that Jack is
  A. ashamed of not watching the kids more closely.
  B. annoyed that Mrs. Morris keeps thanking him.
  C. extremely proud of himself for saving Amy.
  D. thankful that his teacher gave good advice.

It was late spring, and that meant it was time for the fitness exams at Nathan's school. During physical education class, students lined up to do short sprints. The P.E. teacher, Mr. Albers, stood with a stopwatch, keeping time and making notes on his clipboard.

"Ready, set, go!" said Mr. Albers. Nathan's friends had done really well. When it was Nathan's turn, he was sure he would do well. After all, he spent most Saturday and Sunday mornings on long runs with his dad.

But Nathan was in for a surprise. His time was worse than Joey, Brit, and Trevor's. In fact, his was one of the worst times in the whole class.

Over dinner, Nathan told his dad what had happened. "You've always called me a strong runner," Nathan said.

"You are," Nathan's dad said. Then he asked, "Do you have any idea what kind of running you'll do in P.E. tomorrow?"

Nathan didn't know. Besides, that seemed like a strange question to ask. Nathan didn't really care what they'd be doing tomorrow. He felt like a complete failure.

"All right," began Mr. Albers the next day. "Today you're running long distance." Great, thought Nathan, rolling his eyes.

Moments later, Nathan and his classmates were off. After the first lap around the track, Nathan passed Joey. Soon, he passed Trevor and Brit as well. Suddenly Nathan realized he was ahead of everyone. "You're quite a long-distance runner," Mr. Albers said to him when he finished. "Would you consider joining the cross-country team next year?"

Nathan smiled. His father had been right after all. He was a strong runner — a strong long-distance runner.

22. Which words from the story show that Nathan was confident about himself?
   A. "Great, thought Nathan, rolling his eyes."
   B. "He felt like a complete failure."
   C. ". . . Nathan was in for a surprise."
   D. ". . . he was sure he would do well."

23. How does the writer show that Mr. Albers sees Nathan's skill?
   A. Mr. Albers encourages everyone to join the cross-country team.
   B. Mr. Albers tells Nathan he's quite a long-distance runner.
   C. Mr. Albers writes something down on a clipboard.
   D. Mr. Albers tells Nathan that he is not a sprinter.

24. If this story continued, how would Nathan's dad respond to Nathan's long-distance experience?
   A. He would be pleased Nathan did well.
   B. He would be completely surprised.
   C. He would want Nathan to try harder.
   D. He would want to visit the P.E. class.

When May spotted the bighorn sheep on the ridge, she thought she would just walk over and watch them for awhile. She must have misjudged the distance in the clear desert air, though. It took her quite some time to reach the sheep, and then she couldn't find her way back to the trail. May couldn't believe she'd been so foolish. She remembered that there was a creek to the south, which would lead back to her camp. As soon as she figured out which way was south, she started walking in that direction.

25. May probably found her way to the creek by
   A. asking someone for directions.
   B. following the tracks of the bighorn sheep.
   C. using a compass to tell which way is south.
   D. wandering around until she found the trail.

Sam tripped over a toy truck and caught himself just before he tumbled down the stairs. Breathing hard, he took a good look around him. Toys were scattered across the floor in every direction. His little brother and two cousins were playing with still more toys. Sam had been trying to get them to clean up for an hour, but all the kids wanted to do was play games. He was running out of patience, and his parents would be home soon. Suddenly, he had a wonderful idea. "Ok, kids, it's time to play a new game!"

26. What is Sam's new game probably about?
   A. having fun while cleaning the house
   B. distracting the kids while Sam cleans
   C. throwing away some of the kids' toys
   D. running around and playing outside

Kelly squirmed as she looked out at the white wall of clouds that surrounded the airplane. During the last trip she took, she had really enjoyed gazing down at the patchwork of fields below. Now, Kelly was finding it hard to sit still without distractions, and she had finished her magazine at least an hour ago. Kelly squirmed a bit more and then sighed when the captain again asked all the passengers to remain in their seats. Just then, Kelly noticed that the woman sitting next to her had several books in the bag she was carrying.

27. What will Kelly probably do for the rest of the trip?
   A. watch the landscape below
   B. talk to the woman next to her
   C. wander around the plane
   D. ask if she can borrow a book

Mastery Test
Literary Response and Analysis
Narrative Analysis:
Author's Technique and Language

Directions for all questions in this test:

Read each passage and answer the questions that follow it. Some items will have no passage. On the answer sheet, fill in the bubble for the answer you think is correct.

Sample Questions:

> "There's nothing here but a bunch of junk," said Larry. He and his sister, Teresa, were wandering around the tables at a yard sale. Teresa wasn't so sure. On one table was a box of old postcards being sold for a nickel each. What Teresa noticed was the stamps on the postcards. Almost all of them were worth at least several dollars each to collectors. She bought the whole box of postcards for five dollars and couldn't wait to get home to check the value of the stamps on the Internet.

1. What is the lesson in this story?
  A. A bird in the hand is worth two in the bush.
  B. Some people can't see the forest for the trees.
  C. A picture is worth a thousand words.
  D. One person's trash is another's treasure.

2. Which of these is an example of third-person narrative?
  A. "These stamps are worth something," I said.
  B. "How much are these postcards?" asked Teresa.
  C. You can find the value of stamps in several ways.
  D. The others had no idea what I had found.

According to legend, the peacock did not always have such beautiful feathers. He was just an average bird who wanted to stand out. When the peacock's wish was granted, and he got his new feathers, he visited his old friends. The pheasant, the swan, and the heron all admitted that the peacock was by far the most beautiful. On his way home, the peacock saw an eagle soaring overhead, as he used to do. Lifting his wings, the peacock tried to rise, but the weight of his new feathers held him down. He knew then that he would no longer fly up to greet the morning but instead walk the ground like a common beast the rest of his life.

1. What lesson can be learned from this story?
   A. There is always someone less fortunate than yourself.
   B. Do not give up freedom for something less important.
   C. The most precious things in life cannot be bought.
   D. Do not take credit for something you did not do.

A couple of years ago, my family went river rafting for the first time. When my father, mother, younger brother Saul, and I climbed into the raft that day, we were excited. My father was the captain, and we were his crew. All was well until we came to our first rapids and nearly capsized. Saul was a nervous wreck, crying and screaming with fright the whole time. After we pulled into peaceful waters, he calmed down and began to boast about conquering the rapids. From then on, every time we hit a rough spot, Saul became a human waterfall, and when we pulled through, he recovered and began to boast.

2. The moral of this story is
   A. do not count your chickens before they are hatched.
   B. foolish curiosity will usually lead to misfortune.
   C. it is easier to be brave when there is no danger.
   D. it is unkind to take advantage of another's fear.

Cyrus was a busy guy with a tight circle of friends. He and his buddies played on the school soccer team and attended the lunchtime book club. They volunteered with other students one Saturday a month to beautify the school environment. When Cyrus was asked to consider being a student counselor for the school's peer-counseling program, he was surprised.

"But you don't even know me," Cyrus told the man behind the desk.

The vice principal smiled. "It's true we have never spoken," he said. "But I know enough about you to know you'd make an excellent counselor."

3. The theme of this story is
   A. you are judged by your actions and the company you keep.
   B. those who have plenty often want more for themselves.
   C. you should not put your trust in outward appearances.
   D. those who are not afraid to ask questions are rewarded.

Whenever a new family moved to Kline Street, it did not take them long to meet Stella Calnagno. Old-timers called Stella "the glue" of the neighborhood. Even before a moving truck was empty, Stella would arrive on the doorstep, her arms brimming with goodies. "Welcome to Kline," she would say warmly. "I've just baked some fresh bread, and I thought you might like some." Immediately, the newcomers felt like a part of the neighborhood.

4. Stella helps to make Kline Street
   A. a famous place for homemade bread.
   B. a welcome place for new people.
   C. a place where people come and go.
   D. a place with lots of old-timers.

Ever since Mr. Murai started teaching at our school, his classroom has become the place to be. Rather than taking his free period off, Mr. Murai stays in his room and talks with us kids. Not only that, he gets to school long before the bell rings for first period. Students know Mr. Murai's door is always open, and many go there, even though he plays strange music. One time a student asked Mr. Murai what kind of music it was. "What?" Mr. Murai said, pretending to be horrified. "You don't know what jazz is?" Everyone can tell that Mr. Murai really enjoys kids. That's probably why he became a teacher.

5. Why does it seem like Mr. Murai enjoys kids?
   A. He gets to school before the bell rings.
   B. He introduces them to strange music.
   C. He spends his free time with them.
   D. He teaches in a creative and fun way.

When Lora Sandoval entered the Beauford Mansion, she felt like she was transported back in time. The historic mansion was part of a home tour, and the place looked as if it hadn't been touched in a hundred years. Lora tiptoed from room to room, pretending to be one of the Beaufords. The rich, carved-wood furniture and dark, velvet curtains were clearly hers. The old light fixtures were turned down low, just the way she liked them. Standing among the old treasures, it was easy to imagine what life must have been like in 1901.

6. How does the story's setting affect Lora?
   A. It stirs her imagination.
   B. It makes her feel old and tired.
   C. It makes her appreciate her own life.
   D. It causes her feel a little selfish.

Lin Xiangru came from a poor family. When he grew up, he became a servant to people in King Zhao's court. Lin became known for being wise and courageous. After helping the king win several victories, Lin was given a position as a ruling official in the king's court. Another official, Chian Po, did not like the king's choice and did his best to ruin Lin's career.

Chian Po believed that people from poor families should not be able to hold a position among the wealthy. Because Lin had a higher rank than Chian, Chian's pride made him even more angry with Lin. Chian made Lin's life difficult by spreading unkind and untrue rumors about Lin.

One day, Lin Xiangru came upon Chian Po on a narrow road. One of them would have to move aside so their chariots could pass. Lin did something very unusual. He pulled his chariot over and allowed Chian to go first. According to custom, Chian was supposed to pull aside because Lin held a higher rank.

The ruling officials with Lin didn't understand. They thought he made a mistake by allowing someone beneath him to go first.

"How can we work together against our enemies if we do not get along? I must show Chian that without his help we will be conquered, but together, we can continue to earn victories," Lin explained.

When Chian Po heard these words, he was humbled. Chian went to Lin and bowed before him. He apologized to Lin and told Lin to do whatever he liked to punish him. Lin bowed next to Chian.

"Let us come together to work for our country," Lin said. The two became great friends and defenders of King Zhao and his people.

7. Which idea in this story can be found in other stories?
   A. Chian Po is an arrogant man who makes trouble.
   B. Lin Xiangru is wise and courageous.
   C. Wisdom is more helpful than wealth and rank.
   D. A man helps the king win many victories.

8. How is Chian Po like characters in other stories?
   A. His pride makes him do things to hurt other people.
   B. He teaches a proud man a lesson by spreading rumors.
   C. He helps his kingdom by being wise and courageous.
   D. He refuses to move aside for Lin Xiangru.

9. What story is most like the story of Lin Xiangru?
   A. A kingdom finds itself in trouble because of an evil band of warriors.
   B. A child falls asleep and wakes up in a strange world.
   C. A boy conquers a great enemy with the help of his wise teacher.
   D. A man earns the respect of his town and becomes a brave leader.

10. Which of these is an example of *simile*?
  A. The children were exhausted.
  B. Her eyes were like jewels.
  C. The cymbals crashed noisily.
  D. He jumped into the icy lake.

11. Which of these is an example of *metaphor*?
  A. The wind danced in my hair.
  B. We heard the clock ticking.
  C. His arms were becoming tired.
  D. The apple pie was heaven.

12. Writers use *onomatopoeia* to
  A. create a "sound picture."
  B. make animals seem like "real people."
  C. exaggerate something.
  D. make an imaginary thing seem real.

13. Which of these is an example of *hyperbole*?
  A. Samantha acted like a child.
  B. Nel wears a uniform at work.
  C. He ran as fast as a cheetah.
  D. She had hair of golden wheat.

14. What is the purpose of *personification*?
  A. It makes the reader laugh.
  B. It gives life to nonliving things
  C. It compares two things.
  D. It shows how people solve a problem.

15. Why would an author use metaphor?
  A. to make the reader laugh at something that normally isn't funny
  B. to give the reader a better idea of what something sounds like
  C. to help the reader understand one thing by comparing it with another
  D. to show the reader how life long ago is completely different from life today

16. What would be the purpose of using personification to describe a tree?
  A. to make it seem very large
  B. to give it human characteristics
  C. to compare it to other plants
  D. to create the sound of the wind in a tree's leaves

17. Why would an author use onomatopoeia to describe a storm?
  A. to give readers an idea of what the storm sounds like
  B. to show readers that the storm is wetter than a real storm
  C. to compare the storm to disasters described in other stories
  D. to help readers understand that storms are important

The children visit Grandmother once a year. When she greets them, she marvels, saying, "You kids are growing like weeds."

---

18. What Grandmother means is that
   A. they should visit her more often.
   B. she can't seem to get them out of the house.
   C. she doesn't want them to leave.
   D. they are growing very quickly.

When the ice-cream man drives his truck through our neighborhood, the children start swarming like bees to honey.

---

19. What happens when the ice-cream truck comes around?
   A. The children are afraid of bees.
   B. The children go straight to the truck.
   C. The children start to make a buzzing sound.
   D. The children keep their ice cream from the bees.

Rebecca had never eaten enchiladas before, so she took a small bite and slowly began to chew. One minute later, it seemed as though her mouth was on fire.

---

20. What is the author trying to tell you about the enchilada?
   A. It was not tasty.
   B. It needed to cool off.
   C. It was spicy hot.
   D. It needed a little water.

The grove of trees was like the family diary. When Bert and Bettie married, they planted the first oak. Then, as each child was born, they planted another. When these children grew up, they continued the tradition.

---

21. The author's words create the impression that the grove
   A. was how the family earned a living.
   B. was a way of recording history.
   C. was eventually a successful business.
   D. was growing faster than anyone expected.

"Press the dough out nice and flat," said Dad, who ruled the kitchen when it came to homemade pizza.

"I'm trying," I said. "But it's sticking to my hands."

Before Dad could speak, Fran offered a solution. "Here, June," she said. "Rub a little butter on your hands. That should help."

"Are the tomatoes chopped?" Dad wanted to know.

"Yes they are," said Ramey. "And the cheese is grated too," he said.

"Behold, the foundation," I said after flattening out the dough.

Dad rubbed his hands together. "In twenty minutes, we'll have our pizza," he announced.

---

22. Who is telling the story?
- **A.** Dad
- **B.** Fran
- **C.** June
- **D.** Ramey

"Where did you see it last?" Mom asked. I was looking for my basketball uniform, which was nowhere to be found.

"At last week's game," I said impatiently.

"Let's see," said Dad. "What did you do after the game?"

"I went to dinner with the team. Before that, I changed in the locker room and threw the uniform into my sports bag."

Just then, the phone rang. "It's for you," said Mom.

"Hello?" I said. I sounded very frustrated.

"I thought you'd want to know," said Tim, "that I found your uniform in my bag. I'll throw it in the wash and bring it over before tonight's game, okay?"

---

23. You can tell this story is written in first person because
- **A.** there are two or more characters in the story.
- **B.** the story is being told by one of the characters.
- **C.** there is dialogue and conversation in the story.
- **D.** you know what each of the characters is thinking.

24. You can tell when a story is written in the third person because
- **A.** someone other than a character is telling the story.
- **B.** there are at least three people in the story.
- **C.** the story is being told by one of three characters.
- **D.** there is dialogue and conversation in the story.

First Steps Concert—Story 1

Jason watched with wide eyes as the four singers approached the stage. He had been looking forward to this moment for six weeks. When his choir director, Mr. Nelson, announced that the group First Steps would be performing for the school, Jason almost jumped out of his seat. He had all their CDs and dreamed of singing with the group someday. Mr. Nelson told the class that they could watch the group warm up before the performance, and Jason was the first one in the auditorium. He leaned forward, mesmerized, as they tuned to each other's voices. Suddenly they burst into an old spiritual. Jason had never heard anything so beautiful.

First Steps Concert—Story 2

It was my favorite class of the day. Not only that, Ms. Peeler had asked me to come up with a lesson plan to teach the class. Today was the day I was supposed to present it. I could hardly wait to stand in front of the class and tell them what I had learned. I stayed up until 12 o'clock the night before preparing. When I walked into class, Ms. Peeler pulled me aside. She told me that the school was having a special assembly, and that I would have to wait until next class time to present my lesson. I tried not to act disappointed, but I wanted to cry. As the class filed into the hall, I was the last to leave. I walked slowly to the auditorium and sat in the back row. Some group I'd never heard of called First Steps was going to sing. All I could think about was my lesson.

First Steps Concert—Story 3

Chris, Randy, Mark, and Abel had never performed at a high school before. Abel's high school choir director called him after their last tour. Mr. Nelson suggested that they do a concert for Abel's school. Abel hadn't been back to his old school for ten years. When they arrived, Abel gave the guys a tour of the place. Memories from his past flooded back.

"This was my old locker. My friends and I would meet here after school every Wednesday to have jam sessions. Students would crowd around while we jived it up by singing all kinds of fun stuff."

At the choir room, Abel hugged Mr. Nelson and said, "This is the man who made me fall in love with music." Abel and the group followed Mr. Nelson into the auditorium where students were waiting to listen to them warm up.

25. Why is Jason excited about the concert in the first story?
   A. He gets to go into the auditorium first.
   B. He enjoys music and likes the group's work.
   C. The group sang Jason's favorite spiritual.
   D. The group wanted to hear Jason sing.

26. Why did the girl in the second story go to the concert?
   A. She loved listening to music and was a part of the choir.
   B. The teacher gave only certain students permission to go.
   C. She was uninterested in teaching the class that day.
   D. The school was having an assembly, and she had to go.

27. How is Abel's point of view in the third story different from the girl in the second story?
   A. Abel was pleased and the girl wasn't.
   B. The girl wanted to be there but Abel didn't.
   C. Abel was nervous but the girl was calm.
   D. The girl enjoyed the concert but Abel didn't.

28. Read these lines from a poem by Emily Dickinson.

The Wind begun to knead the
   Grass—
As Women do a Dough—

Why do you think she wrote this way?
A. to confuse the reader about the poem
B. to create a picture in the reader's mind
C. to show how bread used to be made
D. to make the reader feel a sense of danger

29. What feeling is created in these lines from a poem by Herman Melville?

When ocean-clouds over inland
   hills
Sweep storming in late autumn
   brown,

A. dismal
B. cheerful
C. peaceful
D. busy

30. Why does the poet repeat the word *knock* so often in these lines of poetry?

What was the constant knock,
   knock, knocking
Waking me before the dawn?

A. to show that the person was expecting a visitor
B. to show that the person had been asleep
C. to show that there is no doorbell
D. to show that the knocking does not stop

Mastery Test
Literary Response and Analysis
Literary Criticism

Directions for all questions in this test:

Read each passage and answer the questions that follow it. Some items will have no passage. On the answer sheet, fill in the bubble for the answer you think is correct.

Sample Questions:

The town was like many other small towns around America. It had tree-lined streets, neat homes, and a comfortable park in the center of town. Not much made Riverside memorable, except for one small fact. It was at the bottom of a huge lake. When the Helmsford Dam had been completed, the lake it formed had covered the town and everything around it. Today, the town is a favorite tourist destination for divers.

---

1. How does the author build surprise in this story?
   A. by talking about tourists
   B. by comparing the town to other towns
   C. by describing the town in detail
   D. by saving important information until the end

2. Which of this additional information about the town of Riverside is *least* believable?
   A. As strange as it sounds, people still live in Riverside.
   B. Using scuba gear, divers can still visit the town.
   C. Many of the houses look almost the same as the day they were flooded.
   D. Swimming through Main Street is one of the favorite activities of the divers.

Mike had been saving money for months to buy tickets to the big game. He finally bought two mid-court seats with an incredible view. Mike was going to take his best friend, Rowen, and he knew the two of them would have a great time. As he was walking out the door to tell Rowen he had gotten the tickets, Mike found his little brother on the stairs with tears in his eyes.

"What's wrong, big guy?" asked Mike.

"I didn't make the basketball team. I hope I didn't let you down, Mike," he said.

Mike paused for a second. Then he said, "Let me down? Of course not. You know what? I just got these great tickets to a game, and I want you to go with me to watch."

1. Mike is an example of someone who
   A. gives up something to help another person.
   B. offers good advice whenever anyone asks him.
   C. becomes the leader of his family and friends.
   D. puts his friends ahead of his family.

Although Isabelle felt sure that she could not possibly tell her mother that she broke her best teapot, she knew it was the right thing to do. Isabelle needed help, so she went to Mama Grand's house. Mama Grand always had just the right words to make things a little easier. Isabelle explained the matter to Mama Grand, who said, "Child, you're worth more to your mama than that old teapot. Tell her the truth, and you'll see how much she loves you."

2. Mama Grand is an example of someone who
   A. knows the value of things.
   B. always seems to give good advice.
   C. fights to save her family.
   D. turns people away from doing the right thing.

The group gathered behind the old warehouse just before dark. Carter had called the meeting to make people see how important it was not to sell their land to Taylor Schultz. Schultz was a businessman who bought up all the land for sale in town. He wanted to make everyone in the town work for him. Carter had to convince everyone that they couldn't sell their land. Freedom from Schultz and his greed was more important than anything right now. As Carter spoke, the group became excited and chanted, "Freedom first! Freedom first!"

3. What does Carter represent?
   A. someone who sacrifices everything for what he believes
   B. an evil villain who thinks little about others
   C. a hero who leads people to fight against evil
   D. someone who gains success though he has very little

As Franco walked down the street, his neighbor, Ms. Watson, stopped what she was doing. She stared with wide eyes as he passed. Franco just nodded his head and walked on.

Franco went downtown, and as he said hello to passers-by, he received the same reaction. They all stopped, stared, and didn't say a word. Franco casually walked a few blocks to the post office.

Margie, the mail clerk, saw Franco from behind. She turned to file some papers, and when she turned around, there stood Franco in front of the counter.

"Morning, Margie. Do you have a package for me?"

Margie stopped and stared. Her face turned white. Her hands began to shake. She stepped back from the counter. Wrapped around Franco's neck and curling around his left arm was a snake at least four feet long.

Margie quickly found the package and slid it across the counter.

Franco said, "How much do I owe you?"

"There's no additional charge. I'm in a hurry. Have to go. See you later, Franco," she stumbled as she walked quickly around the corner and out of sight.

"I wonder what's wrong with her," Franco thought as he laid his hand on his snake and walked away.

4. How does the writer build surprise in the story?
   A. by making the snake try to bite people
   B. by introducing the snake at the end of the story
   C. by giving a good description of Franco's character
   D. by having Franco make the snake hiss at Margie

5. How does the writer suggest that something is different about Franco?
   A. The people who passed by Franco stopped to look at him.
   B. Margie turned white when she saw Franco from behind.
   C. Ms. Watson and Franco stopped to talk to each other.
   D. Franco seemed nervous as he walked through town.

6. How does the writer hint that Franco thought it was normal to have a snake?
   A. Margie became nervous when she saw Franco.
   B. Franco thought Margie behaved strangely.
   C. The people in town greeted Franco and the snake.
   D. Franco didn't notice that people were afraid of the snake.

Kip and his family had just moved from Seattle, Washington, to an apartment in San Diego, California. Kip, who was a little unsure of his surroundings, peered out of his new, tenth-floor bedroom window. His bright green eyes scanned the view, taking it all in. He squinted toward the east. When Kip did this, his freckled nose wrinkled up. "Hey, Mom!" he hollered. "I think I can see my new school from here." Knowing his school was nearby made Kip feel more at home.

7. How does the writer make Kip seem real?
   A. by having him move to a tenth-floor apartment
   B. by giving him such an unusual name
   C. by describing his looks and feelings
   D. by telling you little about his mother

Kirby School District has an annual spelling bee. Students compete against other students in the same grade level, and the winner of each grade level is given the title of champion. Maia had been a champion three years in a row, and she hoped this year would be no different. To prepare, she studied long lists of spelling words. On the day of the event, however, Maia woke with a terrible stomachache. She was also dizzy and too weak to stand up. Regretfully, Maia realized she would not be the winner this year after all.

8. Which of these best describes the plot of this story?
   A. It is unrealistic because no one could win three years in a row.
   B. It is realistic because when you study that hard, you get sick.
   C. It is unrealistic because no schools have spelling bees anymore.
   D. It is realistic because not all stories have happy endings.

Matt and his brother, Austin, were bored one afternoon, so they decided to build a tree house. They borrowed their father's tool chest and gathered together some scraps of wood from behind the garage. In just a few short minutes, the boys had the best tree house you could imagine. There were steps leading up, a front door and doorbell, glass windows, and a peaked, shingled roof.

9. Why is this story not very believable?
   A. They could not have built the tree house in minutes.
   B. There could not have been enough wood behind the garage.
   C. There is no such thing as a tree house with windows.
   D. They could not have known how to build a tree house.

Jaime braced herself as the plane landed. She began to feel giddy as she looked out the window. Just to the north of the airport was the vast ocean. It seemed to be singing to her as it lapped at the shore. Palm trees surrounded the runway like men guarding a fort. The only description she knew of the Cayman Islands was the one in the ad: "Help Wanted. Dive Instructor in the Caribbean. Warm weather, island paradise, good pay."

Jaime had learned to dive when she was ten and had been taking diving classes every summer since. Jaime had decided after her first dive in a small pool that the water was where she was most at home. It was a hidden world she longed to explore. She had dreamed of diving in the ocean, but she knew she would never be able to afford it. When she read the ad, she knew she had to go.

"I need to find the Village Inn. Can you take me there?" Jaime asked a taxi driver. The driver nodded, and Jaime threw her luggage in the back seat.

She arrived at the place where the new instructors lived. After finding her room and unpacking, she quickly changed into her swimsuit and found the dive boat.

"Hi. I'm Mo, the dive master here. I'll show you the first dive that you'll lead this summer." Everyone put on their fins and face masks and prepared to descend.

Jaime couldn't believe how clear the water was. She could see a hundred feet in front of her, and some of the colors were completely new to her. The ocean floor was covered with deep red coral and soft orange sponges. Purple fish with black stripes swam in schools right past her. A shark floated above her head, followed by a huge turtle. Jaime felt like she was on another planet, exploring the secret world she had known only in her dreams.

When she climbed back on the boat, Jaime felt like a different person. "I can't imagine what other wonders are waiting for me," she thought to herself.

10. Carl said he felt like he had been diving after he read the story. What did he probably mean?
  A. The story reminded him of diving last summer.
  B. The story explained how to dive in the ocean.
  C. The story made him see the ocean in his mind.
  D. The story was just like a movie he had watched.

11. Rebecca thought that Jaime was a lot like her. How does Rebecca think of herself?
  A. She loves adventure and exploring underwater.
  B. She prefers swimming in pools because it is safer.
  C. She would rather learn about ocean life from books.
  D. She loves the water, but diving makes her nervous.

12. The story made Bryan want to learn more about the Cayman Islands. Which information from the story probably made Bryan feel this way?
  A. The airport at the Cayman Islands is guarded by armed men.
  B. The Cayman Islands have warm weather and are surrounded by an ocean.
  C. Most people dive in pools at the Cayman Islands.
  D. It is difficult to visit the Cayman Islands by plane because of the weather.

Mastery Test
Vocabulary and Concept Development

General Directions:

This test is made up of 63 questions. Read the directions before each set of questions. Mark all of your answers on the answer sheet. Mark each answer by filling in the bubble for the choice you think is correct. Try these sample questions. Mark your answer on the answer sheet.

Sample Questions:

1. Which of these words means about the same thing as *huge*?
   A. tiny
   B. hug
   C. animal
   D. large

Directions: Find the word that is missing in this sentence.

2. Even though she did not win the contest, Patti did not _____ .
   A. project.
   B. deject.
   C. object.
   D. reject.

Directions: Read each sentence. Choose the word that has the *opposite* meaning of the underlined word. On the answer sheet, fill in the bubble for the answer you think is correct.

1. Kieu Anh's mother likes to tell her, "I remember when that orchard was <u>barren</u> field."
   A. fertile
   B. sandy
   C. grain
   D. fenced

2. The plate looked very <u>fragile</u>, and Alfredo knew better than to handle it roughly.
   A. colorful
   B. durable
   C. expensive
   D. large

3. Richard and Susan were the first two students off the bus; I followed the <u>latter</u>.
   A. driver
   B. order
   C. line
   D. former

Directions: Read each sentence. Choose the word that means the *same thing* as the underlined word in the sentence. On the answer sheet, fill in the bubble for the answer you think is correct.

4. The school principal likes to refer to the <u>peal</u> of the school bell, even though really it is a buzzer.
   A. vibration
   B. ring
   C. shine
   D. metal

5. The student council voted to <u>amend</u> the constitution to permit only two alternate members, instead of three.
   A. decrease
   B. change
   C. delete
   D. concentrate

6. Sofia decided to <u>elevate</u> her feet, hoping that would make them feel better after her two-hour hike.
   A. wrap
   B. soak
   C. lift
   D. rub

Directions: Read each sentence. Choose the correct meaning of the underlined word. On the answer sheet, fill in the bubble for the answer you think is correct.

7. Alicia's grandparents often say their happiness knows no <u>bounds</u> when they visit her.
   A. spring back
   B. limits
   C. on the way

8. The highway workman shook a <u>flag</u> at me, telling me to stop.
   A. become tired
   B. to signal
   C. a banner

9. Much as I liked her, Sharon's manner would sometimes <u>grate</u> on my nerves.
   A. have an annoying effect
   B. shred or grind
   C. part of a fireplace

Directions: Read each sentence. Find the meaning of the underlined word. On the answer sheet, fill in the bubble for the answer you think is correct.

10. Science class is held in two <u>adjoining</u> rooms, one for the laboratory and one for review of the lessons.
    A. connected
    B. without doors
    C. across the hall
    D. additional

11. Manuel had an <u>unquenchable</u> thirst after he ran the 10K race.
    A. unable to drink
    B. not drinking quickly
    C. not enough water
    D. not able to be suppressed

12. Lana <u>deemphasized</u> the work to be done and stressed the fun we would have painting the house.
    A. increased
    B. minimized
    C. encouraged
    D. subtracted

Directions: Read each sentence. Find the meaning of the underlined word. On the answer sheet, fill in the bubble for the answer you think is correct.

13. Martha told Diana to quit making a <u>spectacle</u> of herself in mathematics class.
    A. comedian
    B. public show
    C. eyeglasses
    D. dunce

14. The street called Victor Hugo is an area for <u>pedestrians</u>, and it is lined with shops.
    A. wealthy people
    B. parents with children
    C. parking cars
    D. people walking

15. Chuck was playing his CD so loudly that it was <u>audible</u> in the next room.
    A. unpleasant
    B. could be heard
    C. voluminous
    D. nearly painful

Directions: Read each sentence. Find the meaning of the underlined word. On the answer sheet, fill in the bubble for the answer you think is correct.

16. Mildred always threatened to go <u>incognito</u> to one of the sophomore parties.
    A. after school
    B. disguised
    C. without permission
    D. in place of her sister

17. Marguerite claimed that if she became a famous actress, she would not use a <u>pseudonym</u>.
    A. false name
    B. script
    C. agent
    D. middle initial

18. There is not necessarily a <u>tangible</u> reward for treating others as you would like to be treated.
    A. monetary
    B. heavenly
    C. touchable
    D. sizable

Directions: Read each sentence. Find the meaning of the underlined word. On the answer sheet, fill in the bubble for the answer you think is correct.

19. When she looked back, Jeanne remembered her dad as the <u>embodiment</u> of fatherhood.
    A. poor example
    B. early loss
    C. human form
    D. imagination

20. "Where did you <u>unearth</u> those old clothes of mine?" Sandy's mother asked.
    A. throw out
    B. bury
    C. donate
    D. dig up

21. Rita is a <u>fledgling</u> at scuba diving.
    A. beginner
    B. certified
    C. natural
    D. fearful participant

Directions: Read the blended word in all capital letters. Choose the words that went together to form that blended word. On the answer sheet, fill in the bubble for the answer you think is correct.

22. TELETHON
    A. television + marathon
    B. televise + thing + on
    C. tell + let + ton
    D. tell + station

23. MOTORCADE
    A. motion + arcade
    B. motor + cavalcade
    C. move + torn + cascade
    D. money + tour + trade

24. SMOG
    A. smart + sog
    B. smell + bog
    C. smoke + fog
    D. smash + frog

Directions: Read the words in all capital letters. These words are formed by combining several other words. Find the words that combine to make up the capitalized word. On the answer sheet, fill in the bubble for the answer you think is correct.

25. TGIF
    A. thank + goodness + it's + free
    B. there + goes + interesting + fun
    C. things + gloomy + in + February
    D. thank + goodness + it's + Friday

26. VIP
    A. very + ideal + pupil
    B. visit + initial + problem
    C. very + important + person
    D. valuable + interesting + paper

27. SRO
    A. standing + room + only
    B. stadium + routine + ownership
    C. standard + regular + offer
    D. stop + requiring + occupants

Name _____ Date _____

Directions: Read the words in each box. These are foreign words frequently used in the United States. Find the English meaning of each word or phrase. On the answer sheet, fill in the bubble for the answer you think is correct.

28. | vice versa |
  A. crime fighter
  B. the other way around
  C. a long poem
  D. exactly current

29. | voilà |
  A. That is too loud.
  B. Where are you?
  C. Slow down please.
  D. There it is.

30. | gourmet |
  A. a vegetable like squash
  B. a snobbish person
  C. a government official
  D. a person who enjoys fine foods

Directions: Read each sentence. Choose the correct meaning of the underlined word. On the answer sheet, fill in the bubble for the answer you think is correct.

31. The sailors celebrated as they reached the welcoming entrance to the <u>sound</u>.
  A. channel of water
  B. find the opinions of others
  C. free from damage
  D. vibrations that create noise

32. It took Lynn almost a full day to <u>mount</u> the painting properly.
  A. get up on
  B. fix in a setting
  C. a hill or mountain
  D. post a guard over

33. The interesting tea had a <u>smack</u> of orange flavor.
  A. loud noise
  B. sharp slap
  C. small amount
  D. directly

Directions: Read each sentence. Find the meaning of the underlined words. On the answer sheet, fill in the bubble for the answer you think is correct.

34. The writing on the letter was barely <u>legible</u> as if it had been in Rudy's pocket for a long time.
  A. wrinkled
  B. written
  C. readable
  D. spelled poorly

35. After her English test, Frieda said, "I am ready to <u>frolic</u>. I've done nothing but work for over a week!"
  A. read
  B. have fun
  C. study
  D. sleep

36. Despite Sam's <u>persistence</u> in calling her three nights in a row, Laura turned down his invitation to the party.
  A. charm
  B. allowance
  C. ability
  D. refusal to give up

Directions: Read each sentence. Choose the correct meaning of the underlined word. On the answer sheet, fill in the bubble for the answer you think is correct.

37. After the long climb, the old man said, "I think I should just relax for a <u>spell</u>."
A. magic power
B. name the letters of a word
C. an illness
D. short period of time

38. Despite the height of the cliffs, Audrey was able to <u>scale</u> them.
A. balance
B. a sequence of musical tones
C. outer layer of fish
D. climb

39. The president's guards were able to <u>foil</u> the plot.
A. thin sheet of metal
B. defeat a plan
C. long, thin sword
D. argue against

Directions: Choose the word for the blank that best fits the meaning of each sentence. On the answer sheet, fill in the bubble for the answer you think is correct.

40. We all agreed that the movie wasn't just bad—it was _____ !
A. weak
B. unpleasant
C. poor
D. awful

41. The clever comedian soon had everyone _____ uncontrollably in laughter.
A. giggling
B. uttering
C. chuckling
D. roaring

42. We spent the week exploring the _____ burial grounds.
A. ancient
B. extinct
C. mature
D. old

Directions: Read each sentence. Find the meaning of the underlined words. On the answer sheet, fill in the bubble for the answer you think is correct.

43. Because her test was Friday, Elena said she had to <u>hit the books</u> Wednesday and Thursday.
A. go to the library
B. study
C. organize materials
D. write a book report

44. When Ms. Smith went to France, her students asked her to <u>drop them a line</u>.
A. call on the telephone
B. think about them
C. write to them
D. catch a French fish

45. Jorge was somewhat shy, so he hated to be asked, "<u>Has the cat got your tongue</u>?"
A. Why are you so unfriendly?
B. Are you at all like your brother?
C. Do you dislike cats?
D. Why are you so quiet?

Directions: Read each sentence. Find the sentence that contains an *idiom*. On the answer sheet, fill in the bubble for the answer you think is correct.

46. **A.** Remember to look to the right and to the left before you cross the street.
    B. We have to straighten up the house before Ellen comes home.
    C. Put on your coat and scarf before you go out of the house.
    D. After winning the race, John was ready to paint the town red.

47. **A.** At the last minute, Sharon decided to carry her umbrella to school.
    B. "If you wash the car, it will definitely rain," Anne's brother claimed.
    C. Do not walk on that clean floor before taking off your shoes!
    D. As soon as Jim closed the door, it started raining cats and dogs.

48. **A.** Juanita was so surprised to see Dan that you could have knocked her over with a feather.
    B. Charles said that he lost his appetite when he saw the dirty floor in the restaurant.
    C. "Do your best work on this test," Mr. Harper warned.
    D. Rita loved to dance and sing songs from her native Scotland.

Directions: Read each sentence. Find the sentence that uses an *analogy*. On the answer sheet, fill in the bubble for the answer you think is correct.

49. **A.** The room seemed very dark when we first entered it.
    B. The candle flame was like a warm hearth in the room.

C. In the window a large, leafy, potted plant blocked most of the light.
    D. Dan thought he could smell mint, so he suspected that the candle was scented.

50. **A.** In paintings, sheep usually look fluffy and white on green hills.
    B. Matthew told us that sheep have to be bathed before their wool looks clean.
    C. Ann claims that lambs really are as appealing as they look in pictures.
    D. We might as well be a flock of sheep since we all do and say the same things.

51. **A.** Fire and ice combine about as successfully as Don and Luis do.
    B. Linda's favorite shade of polish was called Purple Plenty.
    C. The manufacturer named the new car's paint "submarine sea teal."
    D. When Rick and Jerry are together, everyone seems to shout nonstop.

Directions: Read each sentence. Find the sentence that contains a *metaphor*. On the answer sheet, fill in the bubble for the answer you think is correct.

52. **A.** The mosquitoes sang in Joe's ears, begging for blood.
    B. Bees buzzed around Rosa and the blooming rose bushes.
    C. Aaron smiled when he saw the bridges over the river.
    D. According to Rachel, the noodle soup was salty.

53. **A.** When the Smiths were on vacation, every day was sunny.
    B. I prefer to drink water rather than sweet things.
    C. The actress's fake jewelry sparkled in the spotlight.
    D. The sky clouded up, getting ready to cry.

Continued on page 154.

54. A. The long hall was dark, dreary.
    B. Sun shone through the south window of the little house.
    C. Thunder and lightning hammered on the roof.
    D. Marlene flung her clothes carelessly over the chair.

Directions: Read each sentence. Find the sentence that contains a *simile*. On the answer sheet, fill in the bubble for the answer you think is correct.

55. A. The ball connected crisply with Lili's bat and shot into center field like a jet.
    B. Hills of red and yellow apples were piled in brown bushel baskets.
    C. Across the gym, the "away" team's fans filled the bleachers—an array of colors, lacking features.
    D. Red tomatoes, flavorful beans, crisp lettuce, even a crispy taco shell—they're nothing without salsa.

56. A. Everywhere people talk with telephones dangling from their ears like earrings.
    B. Television gives us a view out into all the world.
    C. Paul threw a towel over his shoulder and leaped up to the diving board.
    D. After Laura tripped on the stairs, her face took on a bright red glow.

57. A. My grandmother always warned, "Look before you leap."
    B. "No homework" produces smiles like sunshine after a storm.
    C. An apple a day keeps the doctor away.
    D. Softy saying she was tired, Toni suddenly left the room.

Directions: Read each sentence. Find the meaning of the underlined words. On the answer sheet, fill in the bubble for the answer you think is correct.

58. Maria's mother feared she would turn into a <u>couch potato</u> from watching television.
    A. critical viewer
    B. flabby enthusiast
    C. mindless form
    D. horizontal cushion

59. When Roberto was cleaning his room, his father commented, "You remind me of <u>molasses in January</u>."
    A. advancing steadily
    B. sweet and syrupy
    C. bitter and brown
    D. barely moving

60. She coughed slightly, saying, "I must have <u>a frog in my throat</u>."
    A. something keeping a person from speaking clearly
    B. the flu that's been going around
    C. a slight embarrassment
    D. a hunger for a new dish

Directions: Find the meaning of the underlined word or words in each sentence. On the answer sheet, fill in the bubble for the answer you think is correct.

61. The entries in the exhibit had a <u>wide range</u> of quality.
    A. distance between limits
    B. place to practice shooting
    C. grazing land
    D. kitchen stove

62. As soon as the rumors started, Mindy and Joe began to <u>circle the wagons</u>.
    A. join together for protection
    B. attack their enemies
    C. try to escape
    D. work even harder

63. When the semester started, Mr. Lemon said that everyone had a <u>clean slate</u>.
    A. new set of materials
    B. excellent attitude
    C. fresh set of assignments
    D. new record without mistakes

Name _____ Date _____

Directions: Look at the section of a thesaurus. Use this information to answer the questions below.

64. Which of these is another meaning of the <u>adjective</u> form of *willingness*?
    A. laggard
    B. fair
    C. zealous
    D. disposition

65. Which of these is another meaning of the <u>verb</u> form of *indisposition*?
    A. reluctance
    B. grudgingly
    C. inclined
    D. demur

66. Choose another word that could replace the underlined word in the sentence below.

    It seems that Jana simply has a natural <u>tendency</u> to help people in need.

    A. propensity
    B. docile
    C. grudging
    D. dislike

602. WILLINGNESS.—*N.* willingness, disposition, inclination, liking, turn, propensity, leaning, frame of mind, humor, mood, vein, bent, aptitude
    geniality, cordiality, good will; alacrity, readiness, zeal, enthusiasm, earnestness, eagerness.
    assent, etc., 488; compliance. etc., 762.
    volunteer, unpaid worker, amateur, nonprofessional.
    V. be willing, incline, lean to, mind, hold to, cling to; desire, etc., 865; acquiesce, assent, comply with; jump at, catch at, take up, plunge into, have a go at [*colloq.*]
    volunteer, offer, proffer.
    Adj. willing, fain, disposed, inclined, favorable, content, well disposed; ready, forward, earnest, eager, zealous, enthusiastic; bent upon, desirous.
    docile, amenable, easily persuaded, facile, easygoing, tractable, genial, gracious, cordial.
    voluntary, gratuitous, free, unconstrained, spontaneous, unasked, unforced.
    Adv. willingly, fain, freely, with pleasure, of one's own accord; graciously, with a good grace, without demur.

603. UNWILLINGNESS.—*N.* unwillingness, indisposition, disinclination, aversion, averseness, reluctance; indifference, etc., 866; backwardness, slowness; obstinacy, etc., 606.
    scruple, scrupulousness, delicacy, qualm, shrinking, recoil; hesitation, fastidiousness.
    dissent, etc,.489; refusal, etc. 764.
    V. be unwilling, dislike, etc., 489; refuse, etc.,764.
    Adj. unwilling, loath, disinclined, indisposed, averse, reluctant, opposed, adverse, laggard, backward, remiss, slack, indifferent, scupulous; repugnant, restive, grudging, forced, under compulsion, irreconcilable.
    Adv. unwillingly, grudgingly, with an ill grace; against one's will, against the grain; under protest.

Mastery Test **155**

Mastery Test
Oral Reading Fluency

General Directions

Oral reading fluency is one indicator of a student's reading comprehension. The results of this test should be combined with other formal and informal indicators of a student's comprehension to form an overall assessment of current achievement. See page I-1 for more information.

Three components of fluency are assessed in this test. First, an estimate of the student's reading *rate* is determined. For this measure, it is important to time the reading in seconds. The timing should be inconspicuous; otherwise, students may attempt to read the story too quickly and will make increased numbers of errors. Second, you should record the number of errors made during reading. This will be used to estimate the student's reading *accuracy*. Finally, you will make an overall assessment of the student's *fluency* using the rubric below (or others developed locally).

Time: Record the number of seconds the student takes to read the selection. Begin timing when the student reads the first word of the selection. Record this number on the Score Summary on the Student Record Form.

Errors: Record the number of words the student is unable to read or reads incorrectly. Use the reprinted passage on the Student Record Form to mark these errors as you follow along while the student reads. An error is a misread word, a word left out of the selection, or an extra word inserted in the reading that is not in the selection. Do not count a self-correction as an error. Count all errors, whether or not they change the meaning. It is acceptable to assist students with specific words as they read; however, these should be counted as errors. Do not count minor mispronunciations as errors. Record the number of errors on the Score Summary on the Student Record Form.

Holistic Fluency Rating: Use the rubric below to make an overall assessment of the student's fluency. Make this rating immediately after the student completes the reading.

Fluent: The student reads in phrases, generally long meaningful phrases; some errors are likely, but they do not significantly detract from the overall flow of the reading or the selection's meaning; intonation and expression are generally appropriate.

Somewhat Fluent: The student generally reads in short phrases and/or word groupings of limited length (some word-by-word reading may be shown); some word groupings are not consistent with the overall meaning or flow of the passage; at least several errors are made, but most words are read correctly; expression and intonation are limited and often inconsistent with the selection.

Limited Fluency: The student generally reads word by word; limited word groupings are made and most of these are inconsistent with the selection's meaning or flow; multiple errors are made; expression is weak or nonexistent.

Specific Directions

SAY: **Look at this short story. Read it out loud to me. Read it the way you would read it to a friend. If you come to a word you don't know, try your best. Keep reading until you reach the end.**

Follow the reading with the copy on the Student Record Form, and keep track of errors. Also record the number of seconds the student takes. If students stop reading or stumble with a word, encourage them to go on. Help them with an individual word only after waiting several seconds for them to continue.

Oral Fluency Tests — Student Record Form

Student Passage: Mark student errors

David eagerly awaited opening night of his school play. He had auditioned for the play and, to his surprise, got one of the lead roles. He had never acted before, but he loved the theatre and had a natural talent for performing.

Although he rehearsed with the cast for several weeks and knew his lines well, he was nervous about speaking in front of an audience. What if he forgot a line or people couldn't hear him clearly?

But something magical happened when the curtain opened, and his fears were quickly overcome. He felt like he was an important part of a team, and everyone was working together. The result was a wonderful, successful show and a group of very proud performers.

Score Summary

Number of Words in the Selection		**122**
(minus) Number of Errors	–	_____
Number of Correct Words	=	_____
(divide by) Time (in seconds)	÷	_____
Correct Words per Second	=	_____
(multiply by)	×	**60**
Oral Reading Rate (Correct Words per Minute)	=	_____

Oral Reading Accuracy   =   _____
(# Correct Words / # Words in the Selection)

Holistic Fluency Rating: **Fluent**   _____

Somewhat Fluent _____

Limited Fluency _____

Oral Fluency Tests — Student Passage

David eagerly awaited opening night of his school play. He had auditioned for the play and, to his surprise, got one of the lead roles. He had never acted before, but he loved the theatre and had a natural talent for performing.

Although he rehearsed with the cast for several weeks and knew his lines well, he was nervous about speaking in front of an audience. What if he forgot a line or people couldn't hear him clearly?

But something magical happened when the curtain opened, and his fears were quickly overcome. He felt like he was an important part of a team, and everyone was working together. The result was a wonderful, successful show and a group of very proud performers.

Name _____ Date _____

Diagnostic Test
Reading Comprehension

Using and Analyzing Structural Feature	No. Correct	Evaluating Text	No. Correct	Locating and Using Information	No. Correct

Samples:
1. Ⓐ ● Ⓒ Ⓓ
2. Ⓐ Ⓑ ● Ⓓ

Samples:
1. Ⓐ ● Ⓒ Ⓓ
2. ● Ⓑ Ⓒ Ⓓ

Samples:
1. Ⓐ Ⓑ ● Ⓓ
2. Ⓐ ● Ⓒ Ⓓ

Using and Analyzing Structural Feature	Evaluating Text	Locating and Using Information
1. Ⓐ Ⓑ Ⓒ Ⓓ	1. Ⓐ Ⓑ Ⓒ Ⓓ	1. Ⓐ Ⓑ Ⓒ Ⓓ
2. Ⓐ Ⓑ Ⓒ Ⓓ	2. Ⓐ Ⓑ Ⓒ Ⓓ	2. Ⓐ Ⓑ Ⓒ Ⓓ
3. Ⓐ Ⓑ Ⓒ Ⓓ	3. Ⓐ Ⓑ Ⓒ Ⓓ	3. Ⓐ Ⓑ Ⓒ Ⓓ
4. Ⓐ Ⓑ Ⓒ Ⓓ	4. Ⓐ Ⓑ Ⓒ Ⓓ	4. Ⓐ Ⓑ Ⓒ Ⓓ
5. Ⓐ Ⓑ Ⓒ Ⓓ	5. Ⓐ Ⓑ Ⓒ Ⓓ	5. Ⓐ Ⓑ Ⓒ Ⓓ
6. Ⓐ Ⓑ Ⓒ Ⓓ	6. Ⓐ Ⓑ Ⓒ Ⓓ	6. Ⓐ Ⓑ Ⓒ Ⓓ
7. Ⓐ Ⓑ Ⓒ Ⓓ	7. Ⓐ Ⓑ Ⓒ Ⓓ	7. Ⓐ Ⓑ Ⓒ Ⓓ
8. Ⓐ Ⓑ Ⓒ Ⓓ	8. Ⓐ Ⓑ Ⓒ Ⓓ	8. Ⓐ Ⓑ Ⓒ Ⓓ
9. Ⓐ Ⓑ Ⓒ Ⓓ	9. Ⓐ Ⓑ Ⓒ Ⓓ	9. Ⓐ Ⓑ Ⓒ Ⓓ
10. Ⓐ Ⓑ Ⓒ Ⓓ	10. Ⓐ Ⓑ Ⓒ Ⓓ	10. Ⓐ Ⓑ Ⓒ Ⓓ
11. Ⓐ Ⓑ Ⓒ Ⓓ	11. Ⓐ Ⓑ Ⓒ Ⓓ	11. Ⓐ Ⓑ Ⓒ Ⓓ
12. Ⓐ Ⓑ Ⓒ Ⓓ	12. Ⓐ Ⓑ Ⓒ Ⓓ	12. Ⓐ Ⓑ Ⓒ Ⓓ
13. Ⓐ Ⓑ Ⓒ Ⓓ	13. Ⓐ Ⓑ Ⓒ Ⓓ	
14. Ⓐ Ⓑ Ⓒ Ⓓ	14. Ⓐ Ⓑ Ⓒ Ⓓ	
15. Ⓐ Ⓑ Ⓒ Ⓓ	15. Ⓐ Ⓑ Ⓒ Ⓓ	
16. Ⓐ Ⓑ Ⓒ Ⓓ	16. Ⓐ Ⓑ Ⓒ Ⓓ	
17. Ⓐ Ⓑ Ⓒ Ⓓ	17. Ⓐ Ⓑ Ⓒ Ⓓ	
18. Ⓐ Ⓑ Ⓒ Ⓓ	18. Ⓐ Ⓑ Ⓒ Ⓓ	
19. Ⓐ Ⓑ Ⓒ Ⓓ	19. Ⓐ Ⓑ Ⓒ Ⓓ	
20. Ⓐ Ⓑ Ⓒ Ⓓ	20. Ⓐ Ⓑ Ⓒ Ⓓ	
21. Ⓐ Ⓑ Ⓒ Ⓓ	21. Ⓐ Ⓑ Ⓒ Ⓓ	
22. Ⓐ Ⓑ Ⓒ Ⓓ	22. Ⓐ Ⓑ Ⓒ Ⓓ	
23. Ⓐ Ⓑ Ⓒ Ⓓ	23. Ⓐ Ⓑ Ⓒ Ⓓ	
24. Ⓐ Ⓑ Ⓒ Ⓓ	24. Ⓐ Ⓑ Ⓒ Ⓓ	
	25. Ⓐ Ⓑ Ⓒ Ⓓ	
	26. Ⓐ Ⓑ Ⓒ Ⓓ	
	27. Ⓐ Ⓑ Ⓒ Ⓓ	
	28. Ⓐ Ⓑ Ⓒ Ⓓ	
	29. Ⓐ Ⓑ Ⓒ Ⓓ	
	30. Ⓐ Ⓑ Ⓒ Ⓓ	
	31. Ⓐ Ⓑ Ⓒ Ⓓ	
	32. Ⓐ Ⓑ Ⓒ Ⓓ	
	33. Ⓐ Ⓑ Ⓒ Ⓓ	
	34. Ⓐ Ⓑ Ⓒ Ⓓ	
	35. Ⓐ Ⓑ Ⓒ Ⓓ	
	36. Ⓐ Ⓑ Ⓒ Ⓓ	
	37. Ⓐ Ⓑ Ⓒ Ⓓ	
	38. Ⓐ Ⓑ Ⓒ Ⓓ	
	39. Ⓐ Ⓑ Ⓒ Ⓓ	
	40. Ⓐ Ⓑ Ⓒ Ⓓ	
	41. Ⓐ Ⓑ Ⓒ Ⓓ	
	42. Ⓐ Ⓑ Ⓒ Ⓓ	
	43. Ⓐ Ⓑ Ⓒ Ⓓ	
	44. Ⓐ Ⓑ Ⓒ Ⓓ	
	45. Ⓐ Ⓑ Ⓒ Ⓓ	

Name _____ Date _____

Diagnostic Test
Literary Response and Analysis

Student Answer Sheet

Structural Features	No. Correct	Narrative Analysis: Story Elements	No. Correct	Narrative Analysis: Author's Technique and Language	No. Correct

Samples:
1. Ⓐ ● Ⓒ Ⓓ

Samples:	
1. Ⓐ ● Ⓒ Ⓓ	
2. Ⓐ Ⓑ Ⓒ ●	

Samples:
1. Ⓐ Ⓑ ● Ⓓ
2. Ⓐ ● Ⓒ Ⓓ

Structural Features:
1. Ⓐ Ⓑ Ⓒ Ⓓ
2. Ⓐ Ⓑ Ⓒ Ⓓ
3. Ⓐ Ⓑ Ⓒ Ⓓ
4. Ⓐ Ⓑ Ⓒ Ⓓ
5. Ⓐ Ⓑ Ⓒ Ⓓ
6. Ⓐ Ⓑ Ⓒ Ⓓ
7. Ⓐ Ⓑ Ⓒ Ⓓ
8. Ⓐ Ⓑ Ⓒ Ⓓ
9. Ⓐ Ⓑ Ⓒ Ⓓ
10. Ⓐ Ⓑ Ⓒ Ⓓ
11. Ⓐ Ⓑ Ⓒ Ⓓ
12. Ⓐ Ⓑ Ⓒ Ⓓ
13. Ⓐ Ⓑ Ⓒ Ⓓ
14. Ⓐ Ⓑ Ⓒ Ⓓ
15. Ⓐ Ⓑ Ⓒ Ⓓ

Narrative Analysis: Story Elements
1. Ⓐ Ⓑ Ⓒ Ⓓ
2. Ⓐ Ⓑ Ⓒ Ⓓ
3. Ⓐ Ⓑ Ⓒ Ⓓ
4. Ⓐ Ⓑ Ⓒ Ⓓ
5. Ⓐ Ⓑ Ⓒ Ⓓ
6. Ⓐ Ⓑ Ⓒ Ⓓ
7. Ⓐ Ⓑ Ⓒ Ⓓ
8. Ⓐ Ⓑ Ⓒ Ⓓ
9. Ⓐ Ⓑ Ⓒ Ⓓ
10. Ⓐ Ⓑ Ⓒ Ⓓ
11. Ⓐ Ⓑ Ⓒ Ⓓ
12. Ⓐ Ⓑ Ⓒ Ⓓ
13. Ⓐ Ⓑ Ⓒ Ⓓ
14. Ⓐ Ⓑ Ⓒ Ⓓ
15. Ⓐ Ⓑ Ⓒ Ⓓ
16. Ⓐ Ⓑ Ⓒ Ⓓ
17. Ⓐ Ⓑ Ⓒ Ⓓ
18. Ⓐ Ⓑ Ⓒ Ⓓ
19. Ⓐ Ⓑ Ⓒ Ⓓ
20. Ⓐ Ⓑ Ⓒ Ⓓ
21. Ⓐ Ⓑ Ⓒ Ⓓ
22. Ⓐ Ⓑ Ⓒ Ⓓ
23. Ⓐ Ⓑ Ⓒ Ⓓ
24. Ⓐ Ⓑ Ⓒ Ⓓ
25. Ⓐ Ⓑ Ⓒ Ⓓ
26. Ⓐ Ⓑ Ⓒ Ⓓ
27. Ⓐ Ⓑ Ⓒ Ⓓ

Narrative Analysis: Author's Technique and Language
1. Ⓐ Ⓑ Ⓒ Ⓓ
2. Ⓐ Ⓑ Ⓒ Ⓓ
3. Ⓐ Ⓑ Ⓒ Ⓓ
4. Ⓐ Ⓑ Ⓒ Ⓓ
5. Ⓐ Ⓑ Ⓒ Ⓓ
6. Ⓐ Ⓑ Ⓒ Ⓓ
7. Ⓐ Ⓑ Ⓒ Ⓓ
8. Ⓐ Ⓑ Ⓒ Ⓓ
9. Ⓐ Ⓑ Ⓒ Ⓓ
10. Ⓐ Ⓑ Ⓒ Ⓓ
11. Ⓐ Ⓑ Ⓒ Ⓓ
12. Ⓐ Ⓑ Ⓒ Ⓓ
13. Ⓐ Ⓑ Ⓒ Ⓓ
14. Ⓐ Ⓑ Ⓒ Ⓓ
15. Ⓐ Ⓑ Ⓒ Ⓓ
16. Ⓐ Ⓑ Ⓒ Ⓓ
17. Ⓐ Ⓑ Ⓒ Ⓓ
18. Ⓐ Ⓑ Ⓒ Ⓓ
19. Ⓐ Ⓑ Ⓒ Ⓓ
20. Ⓐ Ⓑ Ⓒ Ⓓ
21. Ⓐ Ⓑ Ⓒ Ⓓ
22. Ⓐ Ⓑ Ⓒ Ⓓ
23. Ⓐ Ⓑ Ⓒ Ⓓ
24. Ⓐ Ⓑ Ⓒ Ⓓ
25. Ⓐ Ⓑ Ⓒ Ⓓ
26. Ⓐ Ⓑ Ⓒ Ⓓ
27. Ⓐ Ⓑ Ⓒ Ⓓ
28. Ⓐ Ⓑ Ⓒ Ⓓ
29. Ⓐ Ⓑ Ⓒ Ⓓ
30. Ⓐ Ⓑ Ⓒ Ⓓ

Literary Criticism

Samples:
1. ● Ⓑ Ⓒ Ⓓ
2. Ⓐ Ⓑ ● Ⓓ

1. Ⓐ Ⓑ Ⓒ Ⓓ
2. Ⓐ Ⓑ Ⓒ Ⓓ
3. Ⓐ Ⓑ Ⓒ Ⓓ
4. Ⓐ Ⓑ Ⓒ Ⓓ
5. Ⓐ Ⓑ Ⓒ Ⓓ
6. Ⓐ Ⓑ Ⓒ Ⓓ
7. Ⓐ Ⓑ Ⓒ Ⓓ
8. Ⓐ Ⓑ Ⓒ Ⓓ
9. Ⓐ Ⓑ Ⓒ Ⓓ
10. Ⓐ Ⓑ Ⓒ Ⓓ
11. Ⓐ Ⓑ Ⓒ Ⓓ
12. Ⓐ Ⓑ Ⓒ Ⓓ

Diagnostic Test
Vocabulary and Concept Development

Student Answer Sheet
Phonic Elements

Vocabulary and Concept Development	No. Correct	Vocabulary and Concept Development (continued)	No. Correct	Phonic Elements	No. Correct

Samples:
1. Ⓐ Ⓑ Ⓒ ●
2. Ⓐ Ⓑ ● Ⓓ

Samples:
1. Ⓐ ● Ⓒ Ⓓ
2. Ⓐ Ⓑ Ⓒ ●

Vocabulary and Concept Development	Vocabulary and Concept Development (continued)	Phonic Elements
1. Ⓐ Ⓑ Ⓒ Ⓓ	31. Ⓐ Ⓑ Ⓒ Ⓓ	1. Ⓐ Ⓑ Ⓒ Ⓓ
2. Ⓐ Ⓑ Ⓒ Ⓓ	32. Ⓐ Ⓑ Ⓒ Ⓓ	2. Ⓐ Ⓑ Ⓒ Ⓓ
3. Ⓐ Ⓑ Ⓒ Ⓓ	33. Ⓐ Ⓑ Ⓒ Ⓓ	3. Ⓐ Ⓑ Ⓒ Ⓓ
4. Ⓐ Ⓑ Ⓒ Ⓓ	34. Ⓐ Ⓑ Ⓒ Ⓓ	4. Ⓐ Ⓑ Ⓒ Ⓓ
5. Ⓐ Ⓑ Ⓒ Ⓓ	35. Ⓐ Ⓑ Ⓒ Ⓓ	5. Ⓐ Ⓑ Ⓒ Ⓓ
6. Ⓐ Ⓑ Ⓒ Ⓓ	36. Ⓐ Ⓑ Ⓒ Ⓓ	6. Ⓐ Ⓑ Ⓒ Ⓓ
7. Ⓐ Ⓑ Ⓒ Ⓓ	37. Ⓐ Ⓑ Ⓒ Ⓓ	7. Ⓐ Ⓑ Ⓒ Ⓓ
8. Ⓐ Ⓑ Ⓒ Ⓓ	38. Ⓐ Ⓑ Ⓒ Ⓓ	8. Ⓐ Ⓑ Ⓒ Ⓓ
9. Ⓐ Ⓑ Ⓒ Ⓓ	39. Ⓐ Ⓑ Ⓒ Ⓓ	9. Ⓐ Ⓑ Ⓒ Ⓓ
10. Ⓐ Ⓑ Ⓒ Ⓓ	40. Ⓐ Ⓑ Ⓒ Ⓓ	10. Ⓐ Ⓑ Ⓒ Ⓓ
11. Ⓐ Ⓑ Ⓒ Ⓓ	41. Ⓐ Ⓑ Ⓒ Ⓓ	11. Ⓐ Ⓑ Ⓒ Ⓓ
12. Ⓐ Ⓑ Ⓒ Ⓓ	42. Ⓐ Ⓑ Ⓒ Ⓓ	12. Ⓐ Ⓑ Ⓒ Ⓓ
13. Ⓐ Ⓑ Ⓒ Ⓓ	43. Ⓐ Ⓑ Ⓒ Ⓓ	13. Ⓐ Ⓑ Ⓒ Ⓓ
14. Ⓐ Ⓑ Ⓒ Ⓓ	44. Ⓐ Ⓑ Ⓒ Ⓓ	14. Ⓐ Ⓑ Ⓒ Ⓓ
15. Ⓐ Ⓑ Ⓒ Ⓓ	45. Ⓐ Ⓑ Ⓒ Ⓓ	15. Ⓐ Ⓑ Ⓒ Ⓓ
16. Ⓐ Ⓑ Ⓒ Ⓓ	46. Ⓐ Ⓑ Ⓒ Ⓓ	16. Ⓐ Ⓑ Ⓒ Ⓓ
17. Ⓐ Ⓑ Ⓒ Ⓓ	47. Ⓐ Ⓑ Ⓒ Ⓓ	17. Ⓐ Ⓑ Ⓒ Ⓓ
18. Ⓐ Ⓑ Ⓒ Ⓓ	48. Ⓐ Ⓑ Ⓒ Ⓓ	18. Ⓐ Ⓑ Ⓒ Ⓓ
19. Ⓐ Ⓑ Ⓒ Ⓓ	49. Ⓐ Ⓑ Ⓒ Ⓓ	19. Ⓐ Ⓑ Ⓒ Ⓓ
20. Ⓐ Ⓑ Ⓒ Ⓓ	50. Ⓐ Ⓑ Ⓒ Ⓓ	20. Ⓐ Ⓑ Ⓒ Ⓓ
21. Ⓐ Ⓑ Ⓒ Ⓓ	51. Ⓐ Ⓑ Ⓒ Ⓓ	21. Ⓐ Ⓑ Ⓒ Ⓓ
22. Ⓐ Ⓑ Ⓒ Ⓓ	52. Ⓐ Ⓑ Ⓒ Ⓓ	22. Ⓐ Ⓑ Ⓒ Ⓓ
23. Ⓐ Ⓑ Ⓒ Ⓓ	53. Ⓐ Ⓑ Ⓒ Ⓓ	23. Ⓐ Ⓑ Ⓒ Ⓓ
24. Ⓐ Ⓑ Ⓒ Ⓓ	54. Ⓐ Ⓑ Ⓒ Ⓓ	24. Ⓐ Ⓑ Ⓒ Ⓓ
25. Ⓐ Ⓑ Ⓒ Ⓓ	55. Ⓐ Ⓑ Ⓒ Ⓓ	25. Ⓐ Ⓑ Ⓒ Ⓓ
26. Ⓐ Ⓑ Ⓒ Ⓓ	56. Ⓐ Ⓑ Ⓒ Ⓓ	26. Ⓐ Ⓑ Ⓒ Ⓓ
27. Ⓐ Ⓑ Ⓒ Ⓓ	57. Ⓐ Ⓑ Ⓒ Ⓓ	27. Ⓐ Ⓑ Ⓒ Ⓓ
28. Ⓐ Ⓑ Ⓒ Ⓓ	58. Ⓐ Ⓑ Ⓒ Ⓓ	28. Ⓐ Ⓑ Ⓒ Ⓓ
29. Ⓐ Ⓑ Ⓒ Ⓓ	59. Ⓐ Ⓑ Ⓒ Ⓓ	29. Ⓐ Ⓑ Ⓒ Ⓓ
30. Ⓐ Ⓑ Ⓒ Ⓓ	60. Ⓐ Ⓑ Ⓒ Ⓓ	30. Ⓐ Ⓑ Ⓒ Ⓓ
	61. Ⓐ Ⓑ Ⓒ Ⓓ	31. Ⓐ Ⓑ Ⓒ Ⓓ
	62. Ⓐ Ⓑ Ⓒ Ⓓ	32. Ⓐ Ⓑ Ⓒ Ⓓ
	63. Ⓐ Ⓑ Ⓒ Ⓓ	33. Ⓐ Ⓑ Ⓒ Ⓓ
	64. Ⓐ Ⓑ Ⓒ Ⓓ	
	65. Ⓐ Ⓑ Ⓒ Ⓓ	
	66. Ⓐ Ⓑ Ⓒ Ⓓ	

Phonic Elements

Total Correct Answers = _____ ÷ **33** = _____ **% Correct**

Diagnostic Test
Reading Comprehension

Using and Analyzing Structural Feature — No. Correct

Samples:
1. B
2. C

1. D
2. B
3. C
4. A
5. D
6. C
7. D
8. B
9. C
10. A
11. D
12. C
13. C
14. A
15. C
16. B
17. C
18. A
19. B
20. D
21. B
22. B
23. A
24. C

Evaluating Text — No. Correct

Samples:
1. B
2. A

1. D
2. B
3. B
4. B
5. D
6. D
7. C
8. A
9. D
10. B
11. C
12. A
13. C
14. B
15. D
16. C
17. C
18. C
19. C
20. B
21. A
22. A
23. B
24. D
25. C
26. A
27. D
28. B
29. A
30. D
31. D
32. B
33. C
34. D
35. B
36. D
37. C
38. A
39. D
40. B
41. A
42. C
43. D
44. D
45. A

Locating and Using Information — No. Correct

Samples:
1. C
2. B

1. A
2. D
3. C
4. B
5. D
6. C
7. C
8. A
9. D
10. C
11. A
12. D

Diagnostic Test
Literary Response and Analysis

Structural Features	No. Correct
Samples:	
1. B	
2. (none)	
1. B	
2. D	
3. A	
4. C	
5. C	
6. B	
7. A	
8. C	
9. A	
10. D	
11. B	
12. B	
13. B	
14. D	
15. C	

Narrative Analysis: Story Elements	No. Correct
Samples:	
1. B	
2. D	
1. B	
2. B	
3. D	
4. B	
5. D	
6. C	
7. D	
8. A	
9. B	
10. A	
11. C	
12. A	
13. D	
14. C	
15. A	
16. A	
17. C	
18. B	
19. B	
20. A	
21. D	
22. A	
23. C	
24. C	
25. C	
26. A	
27. B	

Narrative Analysis: Author's Technique and Language	No. Correct
Samples:	
1. C	
2. B	
1. D	
2. B	
3. C	
4. B	
5. A	
6. C	
7. C	
8. B	
9. D	
10. A	
11. C	
12. D	
13. C	
14. B	
15. C	
16. B	
17. D	
18. B	
19. C	
20. D	
21. A	
22. C	
23. A	
24. D	
25. D	
26. A	
27. B	
28. C	
29. B	
30. A	

Literary Criticism

Samples:
1. A
2. C

1. C
2. B
3. C
4. C
5. B
6. A
7. B
8. D
9. B
10. C
11. A
12. C

Diagnostic Test
Vocabulary and Concept Development

Vocabulary and Concept Development	No. Correct

Samples:
1. C
2. C

1. C
2. A
3. C
4. B
5. D
6. B
7. A
8. B
9. B
10. C
11. A
12. B
13. C
14. D
15. A
16. B
17. A
18. D
19. A
20. D
21. C
22. D
23. D
24. A
25. D
26. C
27. D
28. C
29. C
30. A

Vocabulary and Concept Development (continued)	No. Correct

31. D
32. B
33. C
34. C
35. C
36. D
37. C
38. C
39. A
40. D
41. C
42. C
43. B
44. C
45. B
46. B
47. D
48. C
49. B
50. A
51. D
52. C
53. A
54. C
55. A
56. D
57. C
58. D
59. A
60. C
61. A
62. D
63. A
64. C
65. D
66. A

Phonic Elements	No. Correct

Samples:
1. B
2. D

1. D
2. C
3. A
4. B
5. C
6. C
7. B
8. A
9. D
10. D
11. C
12. D
13. C
14. B
15. B
16. B
17. A
18. C
19. A
20. C
21. D
22. B
23. B
24. B
25. C
26. C
27. D
28. C
29. A
30. A
31. B
32. A
33. A

Name _____ Date _____

Mastery Test
Reading Comprehension

Using and Analyzing Structural Feature	No. Correct	Evaluating Text	No. Correct	Locating and Using Information	No. Correct

Samples:

1. ● Ⓑ Ⓒ Ⓓ
2. Ⓐ Ⓑ ● Ⓓ

Samples:

1. Ⓐ Ⓑ ● Ⓓ
2. Ⓐ Ⓑ Ⓒ ●

Samples:

1. Ⓐ Ⓑ Ⓒ ●
2. ● Ⓑ Ⓒ Ⓓ

Using and Analyzing Structural Feature	Evaluating Text	Locating and Using Information
1. Ⓐ Ⓑ Ⓒ Ⓓ	1. Ⓐ Ⓑ Ⓒ Ⓓ	1. Ⓐ Ⓑ Ⓒ Ⓓ
2. Ⓐ Ⓑ Ⓒ Ⓓ	2. Ⓐ Ⓑ Ⓒ Ⓓ	2. Ⓐ Ⓑ Ⓒ Ⓓ
3. Ⓐ Ⓑ Ⓒ Ⓓ	3. Ⓐ Ⓑ Ⓒ Ⓓ	3. Ⓐ Ⓑ Ⓒ Ⓓ
4. Ⓐ Ⓑ Ⓒ Ⓓ	4. Ⓐ Ⓑ Ⓒ Ⓓ	4. Ⓐ Ⓑ Ⓒ Ⓓ
5. Ⓐ Ⓑ Ⓒ Ⓓ	5. Ⓐ Ⓑ Ⓒ Ⓓ	5. Ⓐ Ⓑ Ⓒ Ⓓ
6. Ⓐ Ⓑ Ⓒ Ⓓ	6. Ⓐ Ⓑ Ⓒ Ⓓ	6. Ⓐ Ⓑ Ⓒ Ⓓ
7. Ⓐ Ⓑ Ⓒ Ⓓ	7. Ⓐ Ⓑ Ⓒ Ⓓ	7. Ⓐ Ⓑ Ⓒ Ⓓ
8. Ⓐ Ⓑ Ⓒ Ⓓ	8. Ⓐ Ⓑ Ⓒ Ⓓ	8. Ⓐ Ⓑ Ⓒ Ⓓ
9. Ⓐ Ⓑ Ⓒ Ⓓ	9. Ⓐ Ⓑ Ⓒ Ⓓ	9. Ⓐ Ⓑ Ⓒ Ⓓ
10. Ⓐ Ⓑ Ⓒ Ⓓ	10. Ⓐ Ⓑ Ⓒ Ⓓ	10. Ⓐ Ⓑ Ⓒ Ⓓ
11. Ⓐ Ⓑ Ⓒ Ⓓ	11. Ⓐ Ⓑ Ⓒ Ⓓ	11. Ⓐ Ⓑ Ⓒ Ⓓ
12. Ⓐ Ⓑ Ⓒ Ⓓ	12. Ⓐ Ⓑ Ⓒ Ⓓ	12. Ⓐ Ⓑ Ⓒ Ⓓ
13. Ⓐ Ⓑ Ⓒ Ⓓ	13. Ⓐ Ⓑ Ⓒ Ⓓ	
14. Ⓐ Ⓑ Ⓒ Ⓓ	14. Ⓐ Ⓑ Ⓒ Ⓓ	
15. Ⓐ Ⓑ Ⓒ Ⓓ	15. Ⓐ Ⓑ Ⓒ Ⓓ	
16. Ⓐ Ⓑ Ⓒ Ⓓ	16. Ⓐ Ⓑ Ⓒ Ⓓ	
17. Ⓐ Ⓑ Ⓒ Ⓓ	17. Ⓐ Ⓑ Ⓒ Ⓓ	
18. Ⓐ Ⓑ Ⓒ Ⓓ	18. Ⓐ Ⓑ Ⓒ Ⓓ	
19. Ⓐ Ⓑ Ⓒ Ⓓ	19. Ⓐ Ⓑ Ⓒ Ⓓ	
20. Ⓐ Ⓑ Ⓒ Ⓓ	20. Ⓐ Ⓑ Ⓒ Ⓓ	
21. Ⓐ Ⓑ Ⓒ Ⓓ	21. Ⓐ Ⓑ Ⓒ Ⓓ	
22. Ⓐ Ⓑ Ⓒ Ⓓ	22. Ⓐ Ⓑ Ⓒ Ⓓ	
23. Ⓐ Ⓑ Ⓒ Ⓓ	23. Ⓐ Ⓑ Ⓒ Ⓓ	
24. Ⓐ Ⓑ Ⓒ Ⓓ	24. Ⓐ Ⓑ Ⓒ Ⓓ	
	25. Ⓐ Ⓑ Ⓒ Ⓓ	
	26. Ⓐ Ⓑ Ⓒ Ⓓ	
	27. Ⓐ Ⓑ Ⓒ Ⓓ	
	28. Ⓐ Ⓑ Ⓒ Ⓓ	
	29. Ⓐ Ⓑ Ⓒ Ⓓ	
	30. Ⓐ Ⓑ Ⓒ Ⓓ	
	31. Ⓐ Ⓑ Ⓒ Ⓓ	
	32. Ⓐ Ⓑ Ⓒ Ⓓ	
	33. Ⓐ Ⓑ Ⓒ Ⓓ	
	34. Ⓐ Ⓑ Ⓒ Ⓓ	
	35. Ⓐ Ⓑ Ⓒ Ⓓ	
	36. Ⓐ Ⓑ Ⓒ Ⓓ	
	37. Ⓐ Ⓑ Ⓒ Ⓓ	
	38. Ⓐ Ⓑ Ⓒ Ⓓ	
	39. Ⓐ Ⓑ Ⓒ Ⓓ	
	40. Ⓐ Ⓑ Ⓒ Ⓓ	
	41. Ⓐ Ⓑ Ⓒ Ⓓ	
	42. Ⓐ Ⓑ Ⓒ Ⓓ	
	43. Ⓐ Ⓑ Ⓒ Ⓓ	
	44. Ⓐ Ⓑ Ⓒ Ⓓ	
	45. Ⓐ Ⓑ Ⓒ Ⓓ	

© Pearson Education, Inc.

Mastery Test
Literary Response and Analysis

Student Answer Sheet

Structural Features	No. Correct	Narrative Analysis: Story Elements	No. Correct	Narrative Analysis: Author's Technique and Language	No. Correct

Samples:
1. Ⓐ Ⓑ ● Ⓓ

Samples:
1. Ⓐ ● Ⓒ Ⓓ
2. Ⓐ Ⓑ Ⓒ ●

Samples:
1. Ⓐ Ⓑ Ⓒ ●
2. Ⓐ ● Ⓒ Ⓓ

Structural Features		Story Elements		Author's Technique	
1. Ⓐ Ⓑ Ⓒ Ⓓ		1. Ⓐ Ⓑ Ⓒ Ⓓ		1. Ⓐ Ⓑ Ⓒ Ⓓ	
2. Ⓐ Ⓑ Ⓒ Ⓓ		2. Ⓐ Ⓑ Ⓒ Ⓓ		2. Ⓐ Ⓑ Ⓒ Ⓓ	
3. Ⓐ Ⓑ Ⓒ Ⓓ		3. Ⓐ Ⓑ Ⓒ Ⓓ		3. Ⓐ Ⓑ Ⓒ Ⓓ	
4. Ⓐ Ⓑ Ⓒ Ⓓ		4. Ⓐ Ⓑ Ⓒ Ⓓ		4. Ⓐ Ⓑ Ⓒ Ⓓ	
5. Ⓐ Ⓑ Ⓒ Ⓓ		5. Ⓐ Ⓑ Ⓒ Ⓓ		5. Ⓐ Ⓑ Ⓒ Ⓓ	
6. Ⓐ Ⓑ Ⓒ Ⓓ		6. Ⓐ Ⓑ Ⓒ Ⓓ		6. Ⓐ Ⓑ Ⓒ Ⓓ	
7. Ⓐ Ⓑ Ⓒ Ⓓ		7. Ⓐ Ⓑ Ⓒ Ⓓ		7. Ⓐ Ⓑ Ⓒ Ⓓ	
8. Ⓐ Ⓑ Ⓒ Ⓓ		8. Ⓐ Ⓑ Ⓒ Ⓓ		8. Ⓐ Ⓑ Ⓒ Ⓓ	
9. Ⓐ Ⓑ Ⓒ Ⓓ		9. Ⓐ Ⓑ Ⓒ Ⓓ		9. Ⓐ Ⓑ Ⓒ Ⓓ	
10. Ⓐ Ⓑ Ⓒ Ⓓ		10. Ⓐ Ⓑ Ⓒ Ⓓ		10. Ⓐ Ⓑ Ⓒ Ⓓ	
11. Ⓐ Ⓑ Ⓒ Ⓓ		11. Ⓐ Ⓑ Ⓒ Ⓓ		11. Ⓐ Ⓑ Ⓒ Ⓓ	
12. Ⓐ Ⓑ Ⓒ Ⓓ		12. Ⓐ Ⓑ Ⓒ Ⓓ		12. Ⓐ Ⓑ Ⓒ Ⓓ	
13. Ⓐ Ⓑ Ⓒ Ⓓ		13. Ⓐ Ⓑ Ⓒ Ⓓ		13. Ⓐ Ⓑ Ⓒ Ⓓ	
14. Ⓐ Ⓑ Ⓒ Ⓓ		14. Ⓐ Ⓑ Ⓒ Ⓓ		14. Ⓐ Ⓑ Ⓒ Ⓓ	
15. Ⓐ Ⓑ Ⓒ Ⓓ		15. Ⓐ Ⓑ Ⓒ Ⓓ		15. Ⓐ Ⓑ Ⓒ Ⓓ	
16. Ⓐ Ⓑ Ⓒ Ⓓ		16. Ⓐ Ⓑ Ⓒ Ⓓ		16. Ⓐ Ⓑ Ⓒ Ⓓ	
		17. Ⓐ Ⓑ Ⓒ Ⓓ		17. Ⓐ Ⓑ Ⓒ Ⓓ	
		18. Ⓐ Ⓑ Ⓒ Ⓓ		18. Ⓐ Ⓑ Ⓒ Ⓓ	
		19. Ⓐ Ⓑ Ⓒ Ⓓ		19. Ⓐ Ⓑ Ⓒ Ⓓ	
		20. Ⓐ Ⓑ Ⓒ Ⓓ		20. Ⓐ Ⓑ Ⓒ Ⓓ	
		21. Ⓐ Ⓑ Ⓒ Ⓓ		21. Ⓐ Ⓑ Ⓒ Ⓓ	
		22. Ⓐ Ⓑ Ⓒ Ⓓ		22. Ⓐ Ⓑ Ⓒ Ⓓ	
		23. Ⓐ Ⓑ Ⓒ Ⓓ		23. Ⓐ Ⓑ Ⓒ Ⓓ	
		24. Ⓐ Ⓑ Ⓒ Ⓓ		24. Ⓐ Ⓑ Ⓒ Ⓓ	
		25. Ⓐ Ⓑ Ⓒ Ⓓ		25. Ⓐ Ⓑ Ⓒ Ⓓ	
		26. Ⓐ Ⓑ Ⓒ Ⓓ		26. Ⓐ Ⓑ Ⓒ Ⓓ	
		27. Ⓐ Ⓑ Ⓒ Ⓓ		27. Ⓐ Ⓑ Ⓒ Ⓓ	
				28. Ⓐ Ⓑ Ⓒ Ⓓ	
				29. Ⓐ Ⓑ Ⓒ Ⓓ	
				30. Ⓐ Ⓑ Ⓒ Ⓓ	

Literary Criticism

Samples:
1. Ⓐ Ⓑ Ⓒ ●
2. ● Ⓑ Ⓒ Ⓓ

1. Ⓐ Ⓑ Ⓒ Ⓓ
2. Ⓐ Ⓑ Ⓒ Ⓓ
3. Ⓐ Ⓑ Ⓒ Ⓓ
4. Ⓐ Ⓑ Ⓒ Ⓓ
5. Ⓐ Ⓑ Ⓒ Ⓓ
6. Ⓐ Ⓑ Ⓒ Ⓓ
7. Ⓐ Ⓑ Ⓒ Ⓓ
8. Ⓐ Ⓑ Ⓒ Ⓓ
9. Ⓐ Ⓑ Ⓒ Ⓓ
10. Ⓐ Ⓑ Ⓒ Ⓓ
11. Ⓐ Ⓑ Ⓒ Ⓓ
12. Ⓐ Ⓑ Ⓒ Ⓓ

Name _____ Date _____

Mastery Test
Vocabulary and Concept Development

Student Answer Sheet
Phonic Elements

Vocabulary and Concept Development	No. Correct	Vocabulary and Concept Development (continued)	No. Correct	Phonic Elements	No. Correct

Samples:
1. (A) (B) (C) ●
2. (A) (B) ● (D)

Samples:
1. (A) ● (C) (D)
2. (A) (B) (C) ●

1. (A) (B) (C) (D)	31. (A) (B) (C) (D)	1. (A) (B) (C) (D)
2. (A) (B) (C) (D)	32. (A) (B) (C) (D)	2. (A) (B) (C) (D)
3. (A) (B) (C) (D)	33. (A) (B) (C) (D)	3. (A) (B) (C) (D)
4. (A) (B) (C) (D)	34. (A) (B) (C) (D)	4. (A) (B) (C) (D)
5. (A) (B) (C) (D)	35. (A) (B) (C) (D)	5. (A) (B) (C) (D)
6. (A) (B) (C) (D)	36. (A) (B) (C) (D)	6. (A) (B) (C) (D)
7. (A) (B) (C) (D)	37. (A) (B) (C) (D)	7. (A) (B) (C) (D)
8. (A) (B) (C) (D)	38. (A) (B) (C) (D)	8. (A) (B) (C) (D)
9. (A) (B) (C) (D)	39. (A) (B) (C) (D)	9. (A) (B) (C) (D)
10. (A) (B) (C) (D)	40. (A) (B) (C) (D)	10. (A) (B) (C) (D)
11. (A) (B) (C) (D)	41. (A) (B) (C) (D)	11. (A) (B) (C) (D)
12. (A) (B) (C) (D)	42. (A) (B) (C) (D)	12. (A) (B) (C) (D)
13. (A) (B) (C) (D)	43. (A) (B) (C) (D)	13. (A) (B) (C) (D)
14. (A) (B) (C) (D)	44. (A) (B) (C) (D)	14. (A) (B) (C) (D)
15. (A) (B) (C) (D)	45. (A) (B) (C) (D)	15. (A) (B) (C) (D)
16. (A) (B) (C) (D)	46. (A) (B) (C) (D)	16. (A) (B) (C) (D)
17. (A) (B) (C) (D)	47. (A) (B) (C) (D)	17. (A) (B) (C) (D)
18. (A) (B) (C) (D)	48. (A) (B) (C) (D)	18. (A) (B) (C) (D)
19. (A) (B) (C) (D)	49. (A) (B) (C) (D)	19. (A) (B) (C) (D)
20. (A) (B) (C) (D)	50. (A) (B) (C) (D)	20. (A) (B) (C) (D)
21. (A) (B) (C) (D)	51. (A) (B) (C) (D)	21. (A) (B) (C) (D)
22. (A) (B) (C) (D)	52. (A) (B) (C) (D)	22. (A) (B) (C) (D)
23. (A) (B) (C) (D)	53. (A) (B) (C) (D)	23. (A) (B) (C) (D)
24. (A) (B) (C) (D)	54. (A) (B) (C) (D)	24. (A) (B) (C) (D)
25. (A) (B) (C) (D)	55. (A) (B) (C) (D)	25. (A) (B) (C) (D)
26. (A) (B) (C) (D)	56. (A) (B) (C) (D)	26. (A) (B) (C) (D)
27. (A) (B) (C) (D)	57. (A) (B) (C) (D)	27. (A) (B) (C) (D)
28. (A) (B) (C) (D)	58. (A) (B) (C) (D)	28. (A) (B) (C) (D)
29. (A) (B) (C) (D)	59. (A) (B) (C) (D)	29. (A) (B) (C) (D)
30. (A) (B) (C) (D)	60. (A) (B) (C) (D)	30. (A) (B) (C) (D)
	61. (A) (B) (C) (D)	31. (A) (B) (C) (D)
	62. (A) (B) (C) (D)	32. (A) (B) (C) (D)
	63. (A) (B) (C) (D)	33. (A) (B) (C) (D)
	64. (A) (B) (C) (D)	
	65. (A) (B) (C) (D)	
	66. (A) (B) (C) (D)	

Phonic Elements

Total Correct Answers = _____ ÷ **33** = _____ **% Correct**

Mastery Test
Reading Comprehension

Using and Analyzing Structural Feature	No. Correct
Samples:	
1. ● Ⓐ Ⓑ Ⓒ Ⓓ	
2. Ⓐ Ⓑ ● Ⓓ	
1. Ⓐ Ⓑ Ⓒ ●	
2. Ⓐ ● Ⓒ Ⓓ	
3. Ⓐ Ⓑ ● Ⓓ	
4. Ⓐ ● Ⓒ Ⓓ	
5. Ⓐ Ⓑ ● Ⓓ	
6. ● Ⓑ Ⓒ Ⓓ	
7. Ⓐ ● Ⓒ Ⓓ	
8. Ⓐ Ⓑ ● Ⓓ	
9. ● Ⓑ Ⓒ Ⓓ	
10. ● Ⓑ Ⓒ Ⓓ	
11. Ⓐ Ⓑ ● Ⓓ	
12. Ⓐ Ⓑ Ⓒ ●	
13. Ⓐ Ⓑ ● Ⓓ	
14. ● Ⓑ Ⓒ Ⓓ	
15. Ⓐ Ⓑ Ⓒ ●	
16. Ⓐ Ⓑ ● Ⓓ	
17. Ⓐ Ⓑ ● Ⓓ	
18. Ⓐ ● Ⓒ Ⓓ	
19. Ⓐ Ⓑ Ⓒ ●	
20. ● Ⓑ Ⓒ Ⓓ	
21. Ⓐ Ⓑ ● Ⓓ	
22. Ⓐ Ⓑ ● Ⓓ	
23. ● Ⓑ Ⓒ Ⓓ	
24. Ⓐ Ⓑ Ⓒ ●	

Evaluating Text	No. Correct
Samples:	
1. Ⓐ Ⓑ ● Ⓓ	
2. Ⓐ Ⓑ Ⓒ ●	
1. Ⓐ ● Ⓒ Ⓓ	
2. Ⓐ Ⓑ Ⓒ ●	
3. Ⓐ Ⓑ ● Ⓓ	
4. ● Ⓑ Ⓒ Ⓓ	
5. Ⓐ Ⓑ ● Ⓓ	
6. Ⓐ Ⓑ ● Ⓓ	
7. ● Ⓑ Ⓒ Ⓓ	
8. Ⓐ ● Ⓒ Ⓓ	
9. ● Ⓑ Ⓒ Ⓓ	
10. Ⓐ Ⓑ Ⓒ ●	
11. ● Ⓑ Ⓒ Ⓓ	
12. Ⓐ Ⓑ Ⓒ ●	
13. Ⓐ Ⓑ ● Ⓓ	
14. Ⓐ ● Ⓒ Ⓓ	
15. Ⓐ Ⓑ Ⓒ ●	
16. Ⓐ ● Ⓒ Ⓓ	
17. Ⓐ Ⓑ ● Ⓓ	
18. Ⓐ Ⓑ Ⓒ ●	
19. Ⓐ ● Ⓒ Ⓓ	
20. Ⓐ Ⓑ Ⓒ ●	
21. Ⓐ ● Ⓒ Ⓓ	
22. Ⓐ Ⓑ ● Ⓓ	
23. Ⓐ ● Ⓒ Ⓓ	
24. Ⓐ ● Ⓒ Ⓓ	
25. Ⓐ ● Ⓒ Ⓓ	
26. Ⓐ Ⓑ Ⓒ ●	
27. ● Ⓑ Ⓒ Ⓓ	
28. Ⓐ Ⓑ ● Ⓓ	
29. Ⓐ ● Ⓒ Ⓓ	
30. Ⓐ ● Ⓒ Ⓓ	
31. Ⓐ ● Ⓒ Ⓓ	
32. Ⓐ Ⓑ ● Ⓓ	
33. ● Ⓑ Ⓒ Ⓓ	
34. Ⓐ Ⓑ ● Ⓓ	
35. Ⓐ Ⓑ Ⓒ ●	
36. ● Ⓑ Ⓒ Ⓓ	
37. Ⓐ Ⓑ Ⓒ ●	
38. Ⓐ ● Ⓒ Ⓓ	
39. Ⓐ Ⓑ ● Ⓓ	
40. ● Ⓑ Ⓒ Ⓓ	
41. Ⓐ Ⓑ Ⓒ ●	
42. ● Ⓑ Ⓒ Ⓓ	
43. Ⓐ Ⓑ ● Ⓓ	
44. Ⓐ Ⓑ ● Ⓓ	
45. Ⓐ ● Ⓒ Ⓓ	

Locating and Using Information	No. Correct
Samples:	
1. Ⓐ Ⓑ Ⓒ ●	
2. ● Ⓑ Ⓒ Ⓓ	
1. ● Ⓑ Ⓒ Ⓓ	
2. Ⓐ Ⓑ Ⓒ ●	
3. Ⓐ ● Ⓒ Ⓓ	
4. Ⓐ ● Ⓒ Ⓓ	
5. Ⓐ Ⓑ ● Ⓓ	
6. Ⓐ ● Ⓒ Ⓓ	
7. Ⓐ ● Ⓒ Ⓓ	
8. Ⓐ Ⓑ Ⓒ ●	
9. ● Ⓑ Ⓒ Ⓓ	
10. Ⓐ Ⓑ ● Ⓓ	
11. Ⓐ Ⓑ ● Ⓓ	
12. Ⓐ Ⓑ Ⓒ ●	

© Pearson Education, Inc.

Mastery Test
Literary Response and Analysis

Structural Features	No. Correct

Samples:
1. Ⓐ Ⓑ ● Ⓓ

1. Ⓐ Ⓑ Ⓒ ●
2. ● Ⓑ Ⓒ Ⓓ
3. Ⓐ ● Ⓒ Ⓓ
4. Ⓐ Ⓑ ● Ⓓ
5. Ⓐ ● Ⓒ Ⓓ
6. Ⓐ ● Ⓒ Ⓓ
7. Ⓐ Ⓑ Ⓒ ●
8. Ⓐ ● Ⓒ Ⓓ
9. Ⓐ ● Ⓒ Ⓓ
10. Ⓐ Ⓑ ● Ⓓ
11. Ⓐ Ⓑ Ⓒ ●
12. Ⓐ ● Ⓒ Ⓓ
13. Ⓐ Ⓑ Ⓒ ●
14. Ⓐ Ⓑ ● Ⓓ
15. Ⓐ Ⓑ ● Ⓓ
16. ● Ⓑ Ⓒ Ⓓ

Narrative Analysis: Story Elements	No. Correct

Samples:
1. Ⓐ ● Ⓒ Ⓓ
2. Ⓐ Ⓑ Ⓒ ●

1. Ⓐ Ⓑ Ⓒ ●
2. Ⓐ Ⓑ ● Ⓓ
3. ● Ⓑ Ⓒ Ⓓ
4. Ⓐ Ⓑ ● Ⓓ
5. ● Ⓑ Ⓒ Ⓓ
6. Ⓐ Ⓑ Ⓒ ●
7. Ⓐ Ⓑ ● Ⓓ
8. Ⓐ Ⓑ Ⓒ ●
9. Ⓐ ● Ⓒ Ⓓ
10. Ⓐ Ⓑ ● Ⓓ
11. Ⓐ ● Ⓒ Ⓓ
12. ● Ⓑ Ⓒ Ⓓ
13. Ⓐ Ⓑ Ⓒ ●
14. ● Ⓑ Ⓒ Ⓓ
15. Ⓐ Ⓑ Ⓒ ●
16. Ⓐ ● Ⓒ Ⓓ
17. Ⓐ Ⓑ Ⓒ ●
18. ● Ⓑ Ⓒ Ⓓ
19. Ⓐ Ⓑ Ⓒ ●
20. ● Ⓑ Ⓒ Ⓓ
21. Ⓐ Ⓑ Ⓒ ●
22. Ⓐ Ⓑ Ⓒ ●
23. Ⓐ ● Ⓒ Ⓓ
24. ● Ⓑ Ⓒ Ⓓ
25. Ⓐ Ⓑ ● Ⓓ
26. ● Ⓑ Ⓒ Ⓓ
27. Ⓐ Ⓑ Ⓒ ●

Narrative Analysis: Author's Technique and Language	No. Correct

Samples:
1. Ⓐ Ⓑ Ⓒ ●
2. Ⓐ ● Ⓒ Ⓓ

1. Ⓐ ● Ⓒ Ⓓ
2. Ⓐ Ⓑ ● Ⓓ
3. Ⓐ ● Ⓒ Ⓓ
4. Ⓐ Ⓑ ● Ⓓ
5. Ⓐ Ⓑ ● Ⓓ
6. Ⓐ ● Ⓒ Ⓓ
7. Ⓐ Ⓑ ● Ⓓ
8. Ⓐ ● Ⓒ Ⓓ
9. Ⓐ ● Ⓒ Ⓓ
10. Ⓐ ● Ⓒ Ⓓ
11. Ⓐ Ⓑ ● Ⓓ
12. ● Ⓑ Ⓒ Ⓓ
13. Ⓐ Ⓑ ● Ⓓ
14. Ⓐ ● Ⓒ Ⓓ
15. Ⓐ Ⓑ ● Ⓓ
16. Ⓐ ● Ⓒ Ⓓ
17. ● Ⓑ Ⓒ Ⓓ
18. Ⓐ Ⓑ ● Ⓓ
19. Ⓐ ● Ⓒ Ⓓ
20. Ⓐ Ⓑ ● Ⓓ
21. Ⓐ ● Ⓒ Ⓓ
22. Ⓐ Ⓑ ● Ⓓ
23. Ⓐ ● Ⓒ Ⓓ
24. ● Ⓑ Ⓒ Ⓓ
25. Ⓐ ● Ⓒ Ⓓ
26. Ⓐ Ⓑ Ⓒ ●
27. ● Ⓑ Ⓒ Ⓓ
28. Ⓐ ● Ⓒ Ⓓ
29. ● Ⓑ Ⓒ Ⓓ
30. Ⓐ Ⓑ Ⓒ ●

Literary Criticism

Samples:
1. Ⓐ Ⓑ Ⓒ ●
2. ● Ⓑ Ⓒ Ⓓ

1. ● Ⓑ Ⓒ Ⓓ
2. Ⓐ ● Ⓒ Ⓓ
3. Ⓐ Ⓑ ● Ⓓ
4. Ⓐ ● Ⓒ Ⓓ
5. ● Ⓑ Ⓒ Ⓓ
6. Ⓐ Ⓑ Ⓒ ●
7. Ⓐ ● Ⓒ Ⓓ
8. Ⓐ ● Ⓒ Ⓓ
9. ● Ⓑ Ⓒ Ⓓ
10. Ⓐ Ⓑ ● Ⓓ
11. ● Ⓑ Ⓒ Ⓓ
12. Ⓐ ● Ⓒ Ⓓ

Mastery Test
Vocabulary and Concept Development

Answer Key
Phonic Elements

Vocabulary and Concept Development	No. Correct	Vocabulary and Concept Development (continued)	No. Correct	Phonic Elements	No. Correct

Samples (Vocabulary and Concept Development):
1. Ⓐ Ⓑ Ⓒ ●
2. Ⓐ Ⓑ ● Ⓓ

Vocabulary and Concept Development:
1. ● Ⓑ Ⓒ Ⓓ
2. Ⓐ ● Ⓒ Ⓓ
3. Ⓐ Ⓑ Ⓒ ●
4. Ⓐ ● Ⓒ Ⓓ
5. Ⓐ ● Ⓒ Ⓓ
6. Ⓐ Ⓑ ● Ⓓ
7. Ⓐ ● Ⓒ Ⓓ
8. Ⓐ Ⓑ ● Ⓓ
9. ● Ⓑ Ⓒ Ⓓ
10. ● Ⓑ Ⓒ Ⓓ
11. Ⓐ Ⓑ Ⓒ ●
12. Ⓐ ● Ⓒ Ⓓ
13. Ⓐ ● Ⓒ Ⓓ
14. Ⓐ Ⓑ Ⓒ ●
15. Ⓐ ● Ⓒ Ⓓ
16. Ⓐ ● Ⓒ Ⓓ
17. ● Ⓑ Ⓒ Ⓓ
18. Ⓐ Ⓑ ● Ⓓ
19. Ⓐ Ⓑ ● Ⓓ
20. Ⓐ Ⓑ Ⓒ ●
21. ● Ⓑ Ⓒ Ⓓ
22. ● Ⓑ Ⓒ Ⓓ
23. Ⓐ ● Ⓒ Ⓓ
24. Ⓐ Ⓑ ● Ⓓ
25. Ⓐ Ⓑ Ⓒ ●
26. Ⓐ Ⓑ ● Ⓓ
27. ● Ⓑ Ⓒ Ⓓ
28. Ⓐ Ⓑ ● Ⓓ
29. Ⓐ Ⓑ Ⓒ ●
30. Ⓐ Ⓑ Ⓒ ●

Vocabulary and Concept Development (continued):
31. ● Ⓑ Ⓒ Ⓓ
32. Ⓐ ● Ⓒ Ⓓ
33. Ⓐ Ⓑ ● Ⓓ
34. Ⓐ Ⓑ ● Ⓓ
35. ● Ⓑ Ⓒ Ⓓ
36. Ⓐ Ⓑ Ⓒ ●
37. Ⓐ Ⓑ Ⓒ ●
38. Ⓐ Ⓑ Ⓒ ●
39. Ⓐ ● Ⓒ Ⓓ
40. Ⓐ Ⓑ ● Ⓓ
41. Ⓐ Ⓑ Ⓒ ●
42. ● Ⓑ Ⓒ Ⓓ
43. Ⓐ ● Ⓒ Ⓓ
44. Ⓐ Ⓑ ● Ⓓ
45. Ⓐ Ⓑ Ⓒ ●
46. Ⓐ Ⓑ Ⓒ ●
47. Ⓐ Ⓑ Ⓒ ●
48. ● Ⓑ Ⓒ Ⓓ
49. Ⓐ Ⓑ Ⓒ ●
50. Ⓐ Ⓑ Ⓒ ●
51. ● Ⓑ Ⓒ Ⓓ
52. ● Ⓑ Ⓒ Ⓓ
53. Ⓐ Ⓑ Ⓒ ●
54. Ⓐ Ⓑ ● Ⓓ
55. ● Ⓑ Ⓒ Ⓓ
56. ● Ⓑ Ⓒ Ⓓ
57. Ⓐ ● Ⓒ Ⓓ
58. Ⓐ Ⓑ ● Ⓓ
59. Ⓐ Ⓑ Ⓒ ●
60. ● Ⓑ Ⓒ Ⓓ
61. ● Ⓑ Ⓒ Ⓓ
62. ● Ⓑ Ⓒ Ⓓ
63. Ⓐ Ⓑ Ⓒ ●
64. Ⓐ Ⓑ ● Ⓓ
65. Ⓐ Ⓑ Ⓒ ●
66. ● Ⓑ Ⓒ Ⓓ

Samples (Phonic Elements):
1. Ⓐ ● Ⓒ Ⓓ
2. Ⓐ Ⓑ Ⓒ ●

Phonic Elements:
1. Ⓐ Ⓑ Ⓒ ●
2. Ⓐ ● Ⓒ Ⓓ
3. Ⓐ ● Ⓒ Ⓓ
4. Ⓐ Ⓑ Ⓒ ●
5. Ⓐ ● Ⓒ Ⓓ
6. Ⓐ Ⓑ Ⓒ ●
7. Ⓐ ● Ⓒ Ⓓ
8. ● Ⓑ Ⓒ Ⓓ
9. Ⓐ ● Ⓒ Ⓓ
10. ● Ⓑ Ⓒ Ⓓ
11. Ⓐ Ⓑ Ⓒ ●
12. Ⓐ Ⓑ ● Ⓓ
13. Ⓐ Ⓑ ● Ⓓ
14. Ⓐ ● Ⓒ Ⓓ
15. Ⓐ ● Ⓒ Ⓓ
16. Ⓐ ● Ⓒ Ⓓ
17. Ⓐ Ⓑ Ⓒ ●
18. ● Ⓑ Ⓒ Ⓓ
19. Ⓐ ● Ⓒ Ⓓ
20. ● Ⓑ Ⓒ Ⓓ
21. Ⓐ Ⓑ Ⓒ ●
22. Ⓐ Ⓑ Ⓒ ●
23. ● Ⓑ Ⓒ Ⓓ
24. Ⓐ Ⓑ Ⓒ ●
25. Ⓐ Ⓑ Ⓒ ●
26. Ⓐ Ⓑ ● Ⓓ
27. ● Ⓑ Ⓒ Ⓓ
28. Ⓐ Ⓑ ● Ⓓ
29. Ⓐ ● Ⓒ Ⓓ
30. Ⓐ ● Ⓒ Ⓓ
31. Ⓐ Ⓑ Ⓒ ●
32. ● Ⓑ Ⓒ Ⓓ
33. Ⓐ Ⓑ ● Ⓓ